The **Successful Coach's** *Business Development* & **Planning Calendar**

>>———————————————————————<<

2021

Kimberly DuBrul, PCC

Title: The successful coach's business development and planning calendar 2021

ISBN: 978-1-7361637-0-2

Book design by Phoebe Tucker, *Renegade Apothecary: Craft + Design*
Cover Photo + Styling by Phoebe Tucker
www.renegadeapothecary.com

First edition

This book is dedicated to:

My loving family for their humor and support which keeps me going and specifically...

John, for always taking care of us and our home, especially when the pandemic struck and our house was suddenly full. We didn't miss a beat because of you. Thank you for all you do.

Rowan, for being my biggest teacher, causing me to grow and expand mentally and emotionally toward becoming my best.

Joe Joe, for holding me accountable by asking consistently "how's the book coming?" Thank you for caring.

Natalie Marie Collins, who first sparked this idea for me years ago. You are an inspiration.

Phyllis Emmons Black, my professor at Champlain College and forever dear friend, who believed in me way before I ever believed in myself. Thank you for your support then and now.

Kathy and Andrea, my first clients. You let me coach you when I didn't really know what I was doing yet! I'll always be grateful to you both.

A VERY special thanks to those who helped me to turn this book into a reality when I had no idea how to do it!

Phoebe Tucker, for your beautiful design and calm support. Thank you for seeing my vision and holding it with me.

Melissa Martin for so much logistical help in getting the book made into an actual book! I wouldn't have wanted to try doing it without you!

Greg and Julie Gorman, for believing in me, holding me accountable and coaching me to the finish line!

Table of Contents

Welcome!

Thank you for investing in The Successful Coach's Business Development & Planning Calendar. I designed this book to keep you on track with your business all year long. To grow and stretch you so that you can be and do your best.

I invite you to connect with me and others who are using this book on a private Facebook page at **The Coaches Business Plan Book: https://www.facebook.com/groups/thecoachesbusinessplanbook.**

If you have any trouble finding it, email me at: **Kimberly@kimberlydubrul.com.**

I definitely want you there because I will be doing live monthly motivation, how to's, and answering questions on how to best use the book and grow/manage your coaching business. I check in on the group frequently each week to answer questions, as well.

I am an experienced coach, having been in the business for 19 years. I grew my business from scratch and continue to do so to this day. You are in good hands!

Duplicatable and **consistent** actions add up to consistent income. Let this book guide you to the vision you want for your business and your life.

Carve out time each day to work in this book. I suggest Sunday as a day to plan for the week, and that you reserve one day a month, half-day at least, to hold a business retreat with yourself and this book and any other resources that will help you create a successful month ahead (see the *Resources* section for ideas on how to conduct a retreat). Taking this time in your planning will make it seamless to execute each week.

Planning + **execution** = *results*.

Whether you are beginning this book on January 1 or found it at some other point in the year, today is always the best day to start.

Remember, you are not alone. You now belong to a community of like-minded coaches whom all have a goal to be their best and to create their best business, allowing them to serve the perfect clients for them.

I am excited to be on this journey with you. May this be your best year yet!

Kimberly DuBrul, PCC

Mission + *Vision*

Vision Statement

What are your business goals, and where are you headed in the future? The vision statement is about "seeing." Paint the picture, but do it quickly- 35 words or less! What would you ultimately like to achieve? Short, simple, succinct, specific.

Here's mine, as an example:

"To help people to be themselves, at their best. To create and provide the tools, support, programming, and opportunities to guide them to this place that is uniquely theirs."

Mission Statement

Why does your business exist? In 100 words or less, your mission statement is about the "doing" in your industry. What happens from day to day? What do you do for your clients? Weaving in how this impacts the community/world is a plus these days, too.

My mission statement:

"To provide one on one coaching, coaching groups, mastermind groups, and custom training for individuals and companies/teams who want to live and operate optimally. I provide online support and inspiration through social media events, groups, and teleclasses. Also, speaking engagements via Zoom or in person, when possible. To help all ages to recognize, own, and use their strengths to create the life and business they desire."

"Specifically for coaches, to provide guidance, support, inspiration, and accountability around building skills and a successful, profitable business."

Write your own mission and vision statement here:

_____
_____
_____
_____
_____
_____
_____
_____
_____
_____

Yearly *Goals*

When you think about your yearly goals- think **BIG**!

You can see from having gone through 2020 that truly anything can happen and anything is possible. Though there were many unfortunate instances brought about by the pandemic- there are countless examples of business owners who used creativity to turn what looked like misfortune into a bigger win!

One thing I can say for sure, **the world needs you now more than ever**. The world needs **coaches** now more than ever.

Make it a part of your goals this year and this month to solidify that belief in your own mind.

Feel free to add your own categories to your yearly goals- these will get you started. Your yearly goals are not set in stone. These are meant to be worked with all year long. Tweak and adjust each month as you move forward.

Just having goals sketched out that you move forward with will assure you that you are going somewhere! Many decide to go goal-less and that is just like trying to find your way to your destination with no navigation system. Your goals will keep you on track, especially as you work with them monthly and weekly.

Who would you like to spend time with this year? _____
_____

Who would you like to have coaching you this year? _____
_____

What would you like to learn more about this year? _____
_____

What certifications, certificates or credentials would you like to get this year? _____
_____

What would be fun for you? _____
_____

What would make you a better coach? In other words, what personal things do you want to get out of the way? _____
_____

The Year *at a Glance*

JANUARY

S	M	T	W	T	F	S
					1	2
3	4	5	6	7	8	9
10	11	12	13	14	15	16
17	18	19	20	21	22	23
24	25	26	27	28	29	30
31						

FEBRUARY

S	M	T	W	T	F	S
	1	2	3	4	5	6
7	8	9	10	11	12	13
14	15	16	17	18	19	20
21	22	23	24	25	26	27
28						

MAY

S	M	T	W	T	F	S
						1
2	3	4	5	6	7	8
9	10	11	12	13	14	15
16	17	18	19	20	21	22
23	24	25	26	27	28	29
30	31					

JUNE

S	M	T	W	T	F	S
		1	2	3	4	5
6	7	8	9	10	11	12
13	14	15	16	17	18	19
20	21	22	23	24	25	26
27	28	29	30			

SEPTEMBER

S	M	T	W	T	F	S
			1	2	3	4
5	6	7	8	9	10	11
12	13	14	15	16	17	18
19	20	21	22	23	24	25
26	27	28	29	30		

OCTOBER

S	M	T	W	T	F	S
					1	2
3	4	5	6	7	8	9
10	11	12	13	14	15	16
17	18	19	20	21	22	23
24	25	26	27	28	29	30
31						

MARCH

S	M	T	W	T	F	S
	1	2	3	4	5	6
7	8	9	10	11	12	13
14	15	16	17	18	19	20
21	22	23	24	25	26	27
28	29	30	31			

APRIL

S	M	T	W	T	F	S
				1	2	3
4	5	6	7	8	9	10
11	12	13	14	15	16	17
18	19	20	21	22	23	24
25	26	27	28	29	30	

JULY

S	M	T	W	T	F	S
				1	2	3
4	5	6	7	8	9	10
11	12	13	14	15	16	17
18	19	20	21	22	23	24
25	26	27	28	29	30	31

AUGUST

S	M	T	W	T	F	S
1	2	3	4	5	6	7
8	9	10	11	12	13	14
15	16	17	18	19	20	21
22	23	24	25	26	27	28
29	30	31				

NOVEMBER

S	M	T	W	T	F	S
	1	2	3	4	5	6
7	8	9	10	11	12	13
14	15	16	17	18	19	20
21	22	23	24	25	26	27
28	29	30				

DECEMBER

S	M	T	W	T	F	S
			1	2	3	4
5	6	7	8	9	10	11
12	13	14	15	16	17	18
19	20	21	22	23	24	25
26	27	28	29	30	31	

Financial *Business Plan*

This part of the business plan shouldn't replace advice from a CPA, bookkeeper, attorney, or financial advisor. I always suggest that my clients have these professionals on their team, so maybe one of your first bits of homework will be to make sure you have these people lined up to assist you.

I use this outline to guide me in an overall vision. You will find this outline in each monthly section to break this down for each month.

Your months will not likely all break down the same. Depending upon the season, the numbers could go up or down.

Yearly Income

List all of the categories of your income, and how much you plan to receive in each area.

Category	Projected Income

Ideas for additional sources of income: _____
_____
_____
_____
_____
_____
_____
_____

Total projected income: _____

Yearly *Budget*

List all of the categories of your budget, and how much you plan to spend in each area.

Category	Projected Expense
Professional memberships	
Office space	
Assistance	
Your own coaching	
Supplies	
Professional services (CPA, attorney, etc)	
Taxes	
Marketing and advertising	
Fees	

Yearly expenses *(ones that get paid once per year)*: _____

_____

Monthly expenses *(list what they are and amounts)*: _____

_____

Monthly goal to tax account: _____

Total projected expenses: _____

21 *for 2021*

Self-Care *Plan*

How will you keep yourself healthy and energized so that you can be
optimal in your life and your role as a powerful coach?

Monthly *Themes*

You can use a monthly theme to guide your content. The theme should be something that your audience can connect to and will help them to move forward wherever they may see you expressing it. You can also pick a quarterly theme as well, or just have a quarterly theme.

I think it is fun to pick out all of my themes for the year when I do my yearly planning- which is why I included this page at this point in the book.

You always reserve the right to change your mind when you get to that month, but it is interesting to me how often the theme I picked in December for the following August is exactly right on.

In 2020 I did change some of my themes because the world changed so drastically, I felt compelled to be working with something different than what I had originally thought I might. The great news is- it is up to you, and you can do this however you want to do it!

Month	Theme
January	
February	
March	
April	
May	
June	
July	
August	
September	
October	
November	
December	

How To Use This Planner

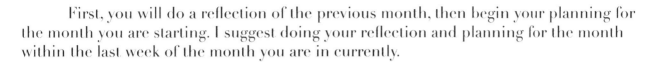

First, you will do a reflection of the previous month, then begin your planning for the month you are starting. I suggest doing your reflection and planning for the month within the last week of the month you are in currently.

Decide on an **income goal** and break down where it will originate. If what you have booked does not match what you want to make that month, you will write down possible ways to create the difference. *Who? What?*

What could you create right now to bring in the income you would like to receive?

Always be thinking about prospects - people referred to you or whom you have met and may want to do business with you.

Keep your list current and visible, so no one falls through the cracks.

Who are you meeting up with, virtually or in-person? What networking events will you attend? Staying visible with people and asking people, "Who do you know that would benefit from working with a great coach right now?" will put you in touch with new clients.

Consistently doing this will result in consistent business.

Create your social media plan by looking at your yearly plan and tweaking it based on your goals for the month.

Think about the next 90 days ahead. What are you working on now that will materialize in 90 days? *Whenever you are struggling with having enough clients, you can USUALLY look back 90 days ago and see your actions or inactions at that time for clues.*

_____

_____

_____

_____

_____

_____

_____

_____

_____

_____

Monthly **Reflection:** *Dec. 2020*

What went well?

_____
_____
_____
_____

What are you most proud of?

_____
_____
_____
_____
_____

What goals did you achieve?

_____
_____
_____
_____
_____

What did not go so well?

_____
_____
_____
_____

What did you learn?

_____
_____
_____
_____

What will you do differently based on what you have learned?

_____
_____
_____

Total income:_____

Your Top Goals: *January*

Monthly Financial Plan

Projected income: _____

Projected or possible income sources: _____

This month's coaching clients: _____

This month's prospects, or people to follow up with: _____

Total coaching slots to be filled: _____

Actual slots filled at the beginning of the month: _____

This month's business expenses: _____

This month's $$ to tax account: _____

This month's projected profit (income - taxes and business expenses): _____

Monthly **Plan:** *January*

Who will you reach out to for help? _____
_____
_____

Who will hold you accountable? _____
_____
_____

In what resources will you invest? _____
_____
_____

What is your income goal, and where will it come from? (names and events)
_____
_____
_____

Who are your top 3 prospects for future business?

     1.

     2.

     3.

What are you creating now to come to fruition over the next 90 days?
_____
_____
_____

How will you stay visible through networking? *(people, events- how? What? When?)*
_____
_____
_____

What results do you intend to get through these networking actions? _____

_____

How many people do you intend to add to your database this month? _____

_____

Consult your plan you made for the year to keep on track.

January Monthly *Plan* Continued

What is your theme for the month? _____

Monthly (or more often) newsletter:
Use the template for creating your newsletter located under resources (pg. 261) to guide you. There are 12 included, so please copy and use (I permit you) if you are doing a more regular newsletter. Mine is weekly as of January 2020, but was monthly for 12 years prior!

Schedule the date or days you will send your newsletter out on your monthly calendar.

Social media plan*: (find clients, increase following) **See the expanded Social Media Plan on page 315 for additional planning guidance!* _____
_____
_____
_____

Where will you post, and how often? _____
_____
_____
_____

What content will you share? *Have a separate notebook for sketching out social media content if necessary.* _____
_____
_____
_____

How often and on what platforms will you go live? *Schedule days, times, and topics into your monthly calendar.* _____
_____
_____
_____

What are your specific goals around your social media actions? _____
_____
_____

Monthly **Overview:** *January*

Sunday	Monday	Tuesday	Wednesday
27	28	29	30
3	4	5	6
10	11	12	13
17	18	19	20
24	25	26	27
31	1	2	3

Thursday	Friday	Saturday	Notes
	1	2	Income goal: _____ Top three prospects: 1. _____
7	8	9	2. _____ 3. _____
14	15	16	Networking events this month: _____ _____ _____
21	22	23	_____ _____ _____
28	29	30	Events to work on this month for the future (90 day outlook): _____ _____ _____
			_____ _____ _____ _____

Week One: *January*

28 *Monday*

29 *Tuesday*

30 *Wednesday*

31 *Thursday*

Top Three Goals:
1.
2.

22 3.

1 *Friday*
2 *Saturday*
3 *Sunday*

Additional Notes:

Ideas

Review + Action Plan Week One: January

Use this page as you prepare for the week ahead, during Sunday planning time.

What went well last week? _____

_____

What did not go so well? _____

_____

What did you learn? _____

_____

What will you do differently this week because of what you learned?

_____

Projects to work on this week and top three actions to take with each:

   (write each activity into your schedule right now)

   1.

   2.

   3.

Prospects to follow up on: _____

_____

Obstacles that could get in your way: _____

_____

Solutions for facing possible obstacles: _____

_____

_____

Three things you are most grateful for:

   1.

   2.

   3.

What is your mantra or affirmation for the week? *(write it and repeat it often!)*

_____

_____

What you are reading this week: _____

_____

What you are listening to this week: _____

_____ 25

Week **Two**: *January*

4 *Monday*

5 *Tuesday*

6 *Wednesday*

7 *Thursday*

Top Three Goals:
1.
2.
3.

8 *Friday*

9 *Saturday*

10 *Sunday*

Additional Notes:

Ideas

Review + Action Plan

Use this page as you prepare for the week ahead, during Sunday planning time.

What went well last week? _____

_____

What did not go so well? _____

_____

What did you learn? _____

_____

What will you do differently this week because of what you learned?

_____

Projects to work on this week and top three actions to take with each:

    (write each activity into your schedule right now)

       1.

       2.

       3.

Prospects to follow up on: _____

_____

Obstacles that could get in your way: _____

_____

Solutions for facing possible obstacles: _____

_____

_____

Three things you are most grateful for:

       1.

       2.

       3.

What is your mantra or affirmation for the week? *(write it and repeat it often!)*

_____

_____

What you are reading this week: _____

_____

What you are listening to this week: _____

Week **Three:** *January*

11 *Monday*

12 *Tuesday*

13 *Wednesday*

14 *Thursday*

Top Three Goals:
1.
2.
30   3.

15 *Friday*

16 *Saturday*

17 *Sunday*

Additional Notes:

Review + Action Plan Week Three: January

Use this page as you prepare for the week ahead, during Sunday planning time.

What went well last week? _____

_____

What did not go so well? _____

_____

What did you learn? _____

_____

What will you do differently this week because of what you learned?

_____

Projects to work on this week and top three actions to take with each:
(write each activity into your schedule right now)

    1.

    2.

    3.

Prospects to follow up on: _____

_____

Obstacles that could get in your way: _____

_____

Solutions for facing possible obstacles: _____

_____

_____

Three things you are most grateful for:

    1.

    2.

    3.

What is your mantra or affirmation for the week? *(write it and repeat it often!)*

_____

_____

What you are reading this week: _____

_____

What you are listening to this week: _____

Ideas

Week **Four:** *January*

18 *Monday*

19 *Tuesday*

20 *Wednesday*

21 *Thursday*

Top Three Goals:
1.
2.
3.

22 *Friday*

23 *Saturday*

24 *Sunday*

Additional Notes:

Review + Action Plan Week Four: January

Use this page as you prepare for the week ahead, during Sunday planning time.

What went well last week? _____

_____

What did not go so well? _____

_____

What did you learn? _____

_____

What will you do differently this week because of what you learned?

_____

Projects to work on this week and top three actions to take with each:

    (write each activity into your schedule right now)

      1.

      2.

      3.

Prospects to follow up on: _____

_____

Obstacles that could get in your way: _____

_____

Solutions for facing possible obstacles: _____

_____

_____

Three things you are most grateful for:

      1.

      2.

      3.

What is your mantra or affirmation for the week? *(write it and repeat it often!)*

_____

_____

What you are reading this week: _____

_____

What you are listening to this week: _____

Ideas

Week **Five**: *January*

25 *Monday*

26 *Tuesday*

27 *Wednesday*

28 *Thursday*

Top Three Goals:

    1.

    2.

    3.

29 *Friday*

30 *Saturday*

31 *Sunday*

Additional Notes:

Review + Action Plan

Use this page as you prepare for the week ahead, during Sunday planning time.

What went well last week? _____

_____

What did not go so well? _____

_____

What did you learn? _____

_____

What will you do differently this week because of what you learned?

_____

Projects to work on this week and top three actions to take with each:
    (write each activity into your schedule right now)
      1.
      2.
      3.

Prospects to follow up on: _____

_____

Obstacles that could get in your way: _____

_____

Solutions for facing possible obstacles: _____

_____

_____

Three things you are most grateful for:
      1.
      2.
      3.

What is your mantra or affirmation for the week? *(write it and repeat it often!)*

_____

_____

What you are reading this week: _____

_____

What you are listening to this week: _____

Ideas

"Your day starts the night before."
Mike Ferry

Monthly Reflection: *January*

What went well?

_____

_____

_____

_____

_____

What are you most proud of?

_____

_____

_____

_____

_____

What goals did you achieve?

_____

_____

_____

_____

_____

What did not go so well?

_____

_____

_____

_____

_____

What did you learn?

_____

_____

_____

_____

_____

What will you do differently based on what you have learned?

_____

_____

_____

_____

Total income: _____

Your Top Goals: *February*

Monthly Financial Plan

Projected income: _____

Projected or possible income sources: _____

This month's coaching clients: _____

This month's prospects, or people to follow up with: _____

Total coaching slots to be filled: _____

Actual slots filled at the beginning of the month: _____

This month's business expenses: _____

This month's $$ to tax account: _____

This month's projected profit (income - taxes and business expenses): _____

Monthly **Plan:** *February*

Who will you reach out to for help? _____

_____

_____

Who will hold you accountable? _____

_____

_____

In what resources will you invest? _____

_____

What is your income goal, and where will it come from? (names and events)

_____

_____

_____

Who are your top 3 prospects for future business?

    1.

    2.

    3.

What are you creating now to come to fruition over the next 90 days?

_____

_____

_____

How will you stay visible through networking? *(people, events- how? What? When?)*

_____

_____

_____

What results do you intend to get through these networking actions? _____

_____

How many people do you intend to add to your database this month? _____

_____

Consult your plan you made for the year to keep on track.

*February Monthly **Plan** Continued*

What is your theme for the month? _____

Monthly (or more often) newsletter:
Use the template for creating your newsletter located under resources (pg. 261) to guide you. There are 12 included, so please copy and use (I permit you) if you are doing a more regular newsletter. Mine is weekly as of January 2020, but was monthly for 12 years prior!

Schedule the date or days you will send your newsletter out on your monthly calendar.

Social media plan*: (find clients, increase following) *See the expanded Social Media Plan on page 315 for additional planning guidance!* _____
_____
_____

Where will you post, and how often? _____
_____
_____

What content will you share? *Have a separate notebook for sketching out social media content if necessary.* _____
_____
_____

How often and on what platforms will you go live? *Schedule days, times, and topics into your monthly calendar.* _____
_____
_____

What are your specific goals around your social media actions? _____
_____
_____

Monthly **Overview:** *February*

Sunday	Monday	Tuesday	Wednesday
31	1	2	3
7	8	9	10
14	15	16	17
21	22	23	24
28			

Thursday	Friday	Saturday	Notes
4	5	6	Income goal: _____ Top three prospects: 1. _____
11	12	13	2. _____ 3. _____
18	19	20	Networking events this month: _____ _____ _____
25	26	27	_____ _____ _____ Events to work on this month for the future (90 day outlook):
			_____ _____ _____
			_____ _____ _____

Week One: *February*

1 *Monday*

2 *Tuesday*

3 *Wednesday*

4 *Thursday*

Top Three Goals:
1.
2.
3.

5 *Friday*

6 *Saturday*

7 *Sunday*

Additional Notes:

Review + Action Plan

Use this page as you prepare for the week ahead, during Sunday planning time.

What went well last week? _____

_____

What did not go so well? _____

_____

What did you learn? _____

_____

What will you do differently this week because of what you learned?

_____

Projects to work on this week and top three actions to take with each:

    (write each activity into your schedule right now)

    1.

    2.

    3.

Prospects to follow up on: _____

_____

Obstacles that could get in your way: _____

_____

Solutions for facing possible obstacles: _____

_____

_____

Three things you are most grateful for:

    1.

    2.

    3.

What is your mantra or affirmation for the week? *(write it and repeat it often!)*

_____

_____

What you are reading this week: _____

_____

What you are listening to this week: _____

Ideas

Week **Two**: *February*

8 *Monday*

9 *Tuesday*

10 *Wednesday*

11 *Thursday*

Top Three Goals:
1.
2.
3.

12 *Friday*

13 *Saturday*

14 *Sunday*

Additional Notes:

Ideas

Review + Action Plan

Use this page as you prepare for the week ahead, during Sunday planning time.

What went well last week? _____

_____

What did not go so well? _____

_____

What did you learn? _____

_____

What will you do differently this week because of what you learned? _____

_____

Projects to work on this week and top three actions to take with each:
   (write each activity into your schedule right now)

    1.

    2.

    3.

Prospects to follow up on: _____

_____

Obstacles that could get in your way: _____

_____

Solutions for facing possible obstacles: _____

_____

_____

Three things you are most grateful for:

    1.

    2.

    3.

What is your mantra or affirmation for the week? *(write it and repeat it often!)* _____

_____

_____

What you are reading this week: _____

_____

What you are listening to this week: _____

_____

Week Three: *February*

15 *Monday*

16 *Tuesday*

17 *Wednesday*

18 *Thursday*

Top Three Goals:

1.
2.
3.

19 *Friday*

20 *Saturday*

21 *Sunday*

Additional Notes:

Review + Action Plan

Use this page as you prepare for the week ahead, during Sunday planning time.

What went well last week? _____

_____

What did not go so well? _____

_____

What did you learn? _____

_____

What will you do differently this week because of what you learned? _____

_____

Projects to work on this week and top three actions to take with each:

    (write each activity into your schedule right now)

      1.

      2.

      3.

Prospects to follow up on: _____

_____

Obstacles that could get in your way: _____

_____

Solutions for facing possible obstacles: _____

_____

_____

Three things you are most grateful for:

      1.

      2.

      3.

What is your mantra or affirmation for the week? *(write it and repeat it often!)* _____

_____

_____

What you are reading this week: _____

_____

What you are listening to this week: _____

58 _____

Ideas

Week **Four:** *February*

22 *Monday*

23 *Tuesday*

24 *Wednesday*

25 *Thursday*

Top Three Goals:

1.

2.

60   3.

26 *Friday*

27 *Saturday*

28 *Sunday*

Additional Notes:

Review + Action Plan Week Four: February

Use this page as you prepare for the week ahead, during Sunday planning time.

What went well last week? _____

_____

What did not go so well? _____

_____

What did you learn? _____

_____

What will you do differently this week because of what you learned? _____

_____

Projects to work on this week and top three actions to take with each:

    (write each activity into your schedule right now)

      1.

      2.

      3.

Prospects to follow up on: _____

_____

Obstacles that could get in your way: _____

_____

Solutions for facing possible obstacles: _____

_____

_____

Three things you are most grateful for:

      1.

      2.

      3.

What is your mantra or affirmation for the week? *(write it and repeat it often!)* _____

_____

_____

What you are reading this week: _____

_____

What you are listening to this week: _____

Monthly Reflection: *February*

What went well?

_____
_____
_____
_____
_____

What are you most proud of?

_____
_____
_____
_____
_____

What goals did you achieve?

_____
_____
_____
_____
_____

What did not go so well?

_____
_____
_____
_____
_____

What did you learn?

_____
_____
_____
_____
_____

What will you do differently based on what you have learned?

_____
_____
_____

Total income: _____ 63

Your Top Goals: *March*

Monthly Financial Plan

Projected income: _____

Projected or possible income sources: _____

This month's coaching clients: _____

This month's prospects, or people to follow up with: _____

Total coaching slots to be filled: _____

Actual slots filled at the beginning of the month: _____

This month's business expenses: _____

This month's $$ to tax account: _____

This month's projected profit (income - taxes and business expenses): _____

Monthly Plan: *March*

Who will you reach out to for help? _____

_____

_____

Who will hold you accountable? _____

_____

_____

In what resources will you invest? _____

_____

_____

What is your income goal, and where will it come from? (names and events) _____

_____

_____

_____

Who are your top 3 prospects for future business?

    1.

    2.

    3.

What are you creating now to come to fruition over the next 90 days? _____

_____

_____

_____

How will you stay visible through networking? *(people, events- how? What? When?)* _____

_____

_____

_____

What results do you intend to get through these networking actions? _____

_____

_____

_____

How many people do you intend to add to your database this month? _____

Consult your plan you made for the year to keep on track.

March Monthly **Plan** Continued

What is your theme for the month? _____

Monthly (or more often) newsletter:

Use the template for creating your newsletter located under resources (pg. 261) to guide you. There are 12 included, so please copy and use (I permit you) if you are doing a more regular newsletter. Mine is weekly as of January 2020, but was monthly for 12 years prior!

Schedule the date or days you will send your newsletter out on your monthly calendar.

Social media plan*: (find clients, increase following) *See the expanded Social Media Plan on page 315 for additional planning guidance!* _____
_____
_____
_____

Where will you post, and how often? _____
_____
_____
_____

What content will you share? *Have a separate notebook for sketching out social media content if necessary.* _____
_____
_____
_____

How often and on what platforms will you go live? *Schedule days, times, and topics into your monthly calendar.* _____
_____
_____
_____

What are your specific goals around your social media actions? _____
_____
_____
_____

Ideas

Monthly Overview: *March*

Sunday	Monday	Tuesday	Wednesday
28	1	2	3
7	8	9	10
14	15	16	17
21	22	23	24
28	29	30	31
4	5	6	7

Thursday	Friday	Saturday	Notes
4	5	6	Income goal:
11	12	13	Top three prospects: 1. 2. 3.
18	19	20	Networking events this month:
25	26	27	
			Events to work on this month for the future (90 day outlook):

Week **One:** *March*

1 *Monday*

2 *Tuesday*

3 *Wednesday*

4 *Thursday*

Top Three Goals:

1.
2.
3.

5 *Friday*

6 *Saturday*

7 *Sunday*

Additional Notes:

Review + Action Plan

Use this page as you prepare for the week ahead, during Sunday planning time.

What went well last week? _____

_____

What did not go so well? _____

_____

What did you learn? _____

_____

What will you do differently this week because of what you learned? _____

_____

Projects to work on this week and top three actions to take with each:

    (write each activity into your schedule right now)

     1.

     2.

     3.

Prospects to follow up on: _____

_____

Obstacles that could get in your way: _____

_____

Solutions for facing possible obstacles: _____

_____

_____

Three things you are most grateful for:

     1.

     2.

     3.

What is your mantra or affirmation for the week? *(write it and repeat it often!)* _____

_____

_____

What you are reading this week: _____

_____

What you are listening to this week: _____

_____

Ideas

Week **Two**: *March*

8 *Monday*

9 *Tuesday*

10 *Wednesday*

11 *Thursday*

Top Three Goals:

  1.
  2.
  3.

12 *Friday*

13 *Saturday*

14 *Sunday*

Additional Notes:

Ideas

Review + Action Plan

Use this page as you prepare for the week ahead, during Sunday planning time.

What went well last week? _____

_____

What did not go so well? _____

_____

What did you learn? _____

_____

What will you do differently this week because of what you learned? _____

_____

Projects to work on this week and top three actions to take with each:

    (write each activity into your schedule right now)

      1.

      2.

      3.

Prospects to follow up on: _____

_____

Obstacles that could get in your way: _____

_____

Solutions for facing possible obstacles: _____

_____

_____

Three things you are most grateful for:

      1.

      2.

      3.

What is your mantra or affirmation for the week? *(write it and repeat it often!)* _____

_____

_____

What you are reading this week: _____

_____

What you are listening to this week: _____

_____ 77

Week **Three:** *March*

15 *Monday*

16 *Tuesday*

17 *Wednesday*

18 *Thursday*

Top Three Goals:

1.

2.

3.

19 *Friday*

20 *Saturday*

21 *Sunday*

Additional Notes:

Review + Action Plan

Use this page as you prepare for the week ahead, during Sunday planning time.

What went well last week? _____

_____

What did not go so well? _____

_____

What did you learn? _____

_____

What will you do differently this week because of what you learned? _____

_____

Projects to work on this week and top three actions to take with each:

    (write each activity into your schedule right now)

      1.

      2.

      3.

Prospects to follow up on: _____

_____

Obstacles that could get in your way: _____

_____

Solutions for facing possible obstacles: _____

_____

_____

Three things you are most grateful for:

      1.

      2.

      3.

What is your mantra or affirmation for the week? *(write it and repeat it often!)* _____

_____

_____

What you are reading this week: _____

_____

What you are listening to this week: _____

_____

Ideas

Week **Four:** *March*

22 *Monday*

23 *Tuesday*

24 *Wednesday*

25 *Thursday*

Top Three Goals:
1.
2.
3.

26 *Friday*

27 *Saturday*

28 *Sunday*

Additional Notes:

Review + Action Plan

Use this page as you prepare for the week ahead, during Sunday planning time.

What went well last week? _____

_____

What did not go so well? _____

_____

What did you learn? _____

_____

What will you do differently this week because of what you learned? _____

_____

Projects to work on this week and top three actions to take with each:

    (write each activity into your schedule right now)

    1.

    2.

    3.

Prospects to follow up on: _____

_____

Obstacles that could get in your way: _____

_____

Solutions for facing possible obstacles: _____

_____

_____

Three things you are most grateful for:

    1.

    2.

    3.

What is your mantra or affirmation for the week? *(write it and repeat it often!)* _____

_____

_____

What you are reading this week: _____

_____

What you are listening to this week: _____

Monthly Reflection: *March*

It's time for your FIRST QUARTER review! Please flip to page 311 to get it done!

What went well?

_____
_____
_____
_____

What are you most proud of?

_____
_____
_____
_____
_____

What goals did you achieve?

_____
_____
_____
_____
_____

What did not go so well?

_____
_____
_____
_____
_____

What did you learn?

_____
_____
_____
_____
_____

What will you do differently based on what you have learned?

_____
_____
_____

Total income: _____

Your Top Goals: *April*

Monthly Financial Plan

Projected income: _____

Projected or possible income sources: _____

This month's coaching clients: _____

This month's prospects, or people to follow up with: _____

Total coaching slots to be filled: _____

Actual slots filled at the beginning of the month: _____

This month's business expenses: _____

This month's $$ to tax account: _____

This month's projected profit (income - taxes and business expenses): _____

Monthly **Plan:** *April*

Who will you reach out to for help? _____

_____

_____

Who will hold you accountable? _____

_____

_____

In what resources will you invest? _____

_____

_____

What is your income goal, and where will it come from? (names and events) _____

_____

_____

_____

Who are your top 3 prospects for future business?

      1.

      2.

      3.

What are you creating now to come to fruition over the next 90 days? _____

_____

_____

_____

How will you stay visible through networking? *(people, events- how? What? When?)* _____

_____

_____

_____

What results do you intend to get through these networking actions? _____

_____

_____

_____

How many people do you intend to add to your database this month? _____

Consult your plan you made for the year to keep on track.

April Monthly **Plan** Continued

What is your theme for the month? _____

Monthly (or more often) newsletter:
Use the template for creating your newsletter located under resources (pg. 261) to guide you. There are 12 included, so please copy and use (I permit you) if you are doing a more regular newsletter. Mine is weekly as of January 2020, but was monthly for 12 years prior!

Schedule the date or days you will send your newsletter out on your monthly calendar.

Social media plan*: (find clients, increase following) *See the expanded Social Media Plan on page 315 for additional planning guidance!* _____
_____
_____
_____

Where will you post, and how often? _____
_____
_____
_____

What content will you share? *Have a separate notebook for sketching out social media content if necessary.* _____
_____
_____
_____

How often and on what platforms will you go live? *Schedule days, times, and topics into your monthly calendar.* _____
_____
_____
_____

What are your specific goals around your social media actions? _____
_____
_____
_____

Ideas

Monthly **Overview:** *April*

Sunday	Monday	Tuesday	Wednesday
28	29	30	31
4	5	6	7
11	12	13	14
18	19	20	21
25	26	27	28

Thursday	Friday	Saturday	Notes
1	2	3	Income goal: Top three prospects: 1.
8	9	10	2. 3.
15	16	17	Networking events this month:
22	23	24	
29	30		Events to work on this month for the future (90 day outlook):

Week One: *April*

29 *Monday*

30 *Tuesday*

31 *Wednesday*

1 *Thursday*

Top Three Goals:

1.

2.

3.

2 *Friday*

3 *Saturday*

4 *Sunday*

Additional Notes:

Review + Action Plan Week One: April

Use this page as you prepare for the week ahead, during Sunday planning time.

What went well last week? _____

_____

What did not go so well? _____

_____

What did you learn? _____

_____

What will you do differently this week because of what you learned? _____

_____

Projects to work on this week and top three actions to take with each:
  (write each activity into your schedule right now)
  1.
  2.
  3.

Prospects to follow up on: _____

_____

Obstacles that could get in your way: _____

_____

Solutions for facing possible obstacles: _____

_____

_____

Three things you are most grateful for:
  1.
  2.
  3.

What is your mantra or affirmation for the week? *(write it and repeat it often!)* _____

_____

_____

What you are reading this week: _____

_____

What you are listening to this week: _____

_____

Ideas

Week Two: *April*

5 *Monday*

6 *Tuesday*

7 *Wednesday*

8 *Thursday*

Top Three Goals:

1.
2.
3.

9 *Friday*

10 *Saturday*

11 *Sunday*

Additional Notes:

Review + Action Plan

Use this page as you prepare for the week ahead, during Sunday planning time.

What went well last week? _____

_____

What did not go so well? _____

_____

What did you learn? _____

_____

What will you do differently this week because of what you learned? _____

_____

Projects to work on this week and top three actions to take with each:

    (write each activity into your schedule right now)

    1.

    2.

    3.

Prospects to follow up on: _____

_____

Obstacles that could get in your way: _____

_____

Solutions for facing possible obstacles: _____

_____

_____

Three things you are most grateful for:

    1.

    2.

    3.

What is your mantra or affirmation for the week? *(write it and repeat it often!)* _____

_____

_____

What you are reading this week: _____

_____

What you are listening to this week: _____

Ideas

Week Three: *April*

12 *Monday*

13 *Tuesday*

14 *Wednesday*

15 *Thursday*

Top Three Goals:

1.
2.
3.

16 *Friday*

17 *Saturday*

18 *Sunday*

Additional Notes:

Review + Action Plan Week Three: April

Use this page as you prepare for the week ahead, during Sunday planning time.

What went well last week? _____

_____

What did not go so well? _____

_____

What did you learn? _____

_____

What will you do differently this week because of what you learned? _____

_____

Projects to work on this week and top three actions to take with each:

    (write each activity into your schedule right now)

      1.

      2.

      3.

Prospects to follow up on: _____

_____

Obstacles that could get in your way: _____

_____

Solutions for facing possible obstacles: _____

_____

_____

Three things you are most grateful for:

      1.

      2.

      3.

What is your mantra or affirmation for the week? *(write it and repeat it often!)* _____

_____

_____

What you are reading this week: _____

_____

What you are listening to this week: _____

_____

Ideas

Week **Four:** *April*

19 *Monday*

20 *Tuesday*

21 *Wednesday*

22 *Thursday*

Top Three Goals:

    1.

    2.

  3.

23 *Friday*

24 *Saturday*

25 *Sunday*

Additional Notes:

Review + Action Plan

Use this page as you prepare for the week ahead, during Sunday planning time.

What went well last week? _____

_____

What did not go so well? _____

_____

What did you learn? _____

_____

What will you do differently this week because of what you learned? _____

_____

Projects to work on this week and top three actions to take with each:

   (write each activity into your schedule right now)

   1.

   2.

   3.

Prospects to follow up on: _____

_____

Obstacles that could get in your way: _____

_____

Solutions for facing possible obstacles: _____

_____

_____

Three things you are most grateful for:

   1.

   2.

   3.

What is your mantra or affirmation for the week? *(write it and repeat it often!)* _____

_____

_____

What you are reading this week: _____

_____

What you are listening to this week: _____

106 _____

Ideas

Week **Five:** *April*

26 *Monday*

27 *Tuesday*

28 *Wednesday*

29 *Thursday*

Top Three Goals:

1.

2.

3.

30 *Friday*
1 *Saturday*
2 *Sunday*

Additional Notes:

Review + Action Plan

Use this page as you prepare for the week ahead, during Sunday planning time.

What went well last week? _____

_____

What did not go so well? _____

_____

What did you learn? _____

_____

What will you do differently this week because of what you learned? _____

_____

Projects to work on this week and top three actions to take with each:

    (write each activity into your schedule right now)

      1.

      2.

      3.

Prospects to follow up on: _____

_____

Obstacles that could get in your way: _____

_____

Solutions for facing possible obstacles: _____

_____

_____

Three things you are most grateful for:

      1.

      2.

      3.

What is your mantra or affirmation for the week? *(write it and repeat it often!)* _____

_____

_____

What you are reading this week: _____

_____

What you are listening to this week: _____

Ideas

"Start by asking the right questions before you start looking for the right answers." Valorie Burton

Monthly Reflection: *April*

What went well?

_____
_____
_____
_____

What are you most proud of?

_____
_____
_____
_____
_____
_____

What goals did you achieve?

_____
_____
_____
_____
_____
_____

What did not go so well?

_____
_____
_____
_____
_____

What did you learn?

_____
_____
_____
_____
_____

What will you do differently based on what you have learned?

_____
_____
_____

Total income: _____

Your Top Goals: *May*

Monthly Financial Plan

Projected income: _____

Projected or possible income sources: _____

This month's coaching clients: _____

This month's prospects, or people to follow up with: _____

Total coaching slots to be filled: _____

Actual slots filled at the beginning of the month: _____

This month's business expenses: _____

This month's $$ to tax account: _____

This month's projected profit (income - taxes and business expenses): _____

Monthly Plan: *May*

Who will you reach out to for help? _____

_____

_____

Who will hold you accountable? _____

_____

_____

In what resources will you invest? _____

_____

_____

What is your income goal, and where will it come from? (names and events) _____

_____

_____

_____

Who are your top 3 prospects for future business?

     1.

     2.

     3.

What are you creating now to come to fruition over the next 90 days? _____

_____

_____

_____

How will you stay visible through networking? *(people, events- how? What? When?)* _____

_____

_____

_____

What results do you intend to get through these networking actions? _____

_____

_____

_____

How many people do you intend to add to your database this month? _____

Consult your plan you made for the year to keep on track.

May Monthly **Plan** Continued

What is your theme for the month? _____

Monthly (or more often) newsletter:
Use the template for creating your newsletter located under resources (pg. 261) to guide you. There are 12 included, so please copy and use (I permit you) if you are doing a more regular newsletter. Mine is weekly as of January 2020, but was monthly for 12 years prior!

Schedule the date or days you will send your newsletter out on your monthly calendar.

Social media plan*: (find clients, increase following) **See the expanded Social Media Plan on* *page 315 for additional planning guidance!* _____
_____
_____
_____

Where will you post, and how often? _____
_____
_____
_____

What content will you share? *Have a separate notebook for sketching out social media content if necessary.* _____
_____
_____
_____

How often and on what platforms will you go live? *Schedule days, times, and topics into your monthly calendar.* _____
_____
_____
_____

What are your specific goals around your social media actions? _____
_____
_____
_____

Monthly Overview: *May*

Monthly Theme: _____

Sunday	Monday	Tuesday	Wednesday
25	26	27	28
2	3	4	5
9	10	11	12
16	17	18	19
23	24	25	26
30	31		

Thursday	Friday	Saturday	Notes
29	30	1	Income goal: Top three prospects: 1.
6	7	8	2. 3.
13	14	15	Networking events this month:
20	21	22	
27	28	29	Events to work on this month for the future (90 day outlook):

Week One: *May*

3 *Monday*

4 *Tuesday*

5 *Wednesday*

Top Three Goals:

1.

2.

3.

7 *Friday*

8 *Saturday*

9 *Sunday*

Additional Notes:

Review + Action Plan Week One: May

Use this page as you prepare for the week ahead, during Sunday planning time.

What went well last week? _____

_____

What did not go so well? _____

_____

What did you learn? _____

_____

What will you do differently this week because of what you learned? _____

_____

Projects to work on this week and top three actions to take with each:

    (write each activity into your schedule right now)

    1.

    2.

    3.

Prospects to follow up on: _____

_____

Obstacles that could get in your way: _____

_____

Solutions for facing possible obstacles: _____

_____

_____

Three things you are most grateful for:

    1.

    2.

    3.

What is your mantra or affirmation for the week? *(write it and repeat it often!)* _____

_____

_____

What you are reading this week: _____

_____

What you are listening to this week: _____

_____

Ideas

Week **Two:** *May*

10 *Monday*

11 *Tuesday*

12 *Wednesday*

13 *Thursday*

Top Three Goals:
1.
2.
3.

14 *Friday*

15 *Saturday*

16 *Sunday*

Additional Notes:

Review + Action Plan

Use this page as you prepare for the week ahead, during Sunday planning time.

What went well last week? _____

_____

What did not go so well? _____

_____

What did you learn? _____

_____

What will you do differently this week because of what you learned? _____

_____

Projects to work on this week and top three actions to take with each:

    (write each activity into your schedule right now)

      1.

      2.

      3.

Prospects to follow up on: _____

_____

Obstacles that could get in your way: _____

_____

Solutions for facing possible obstacles: _____

_____

_____

Three things you are most grateful for:

      1.

      2.

      3.

What is your mantra or affirmation for the week? *(write it and repeat it often!)* _____

_____

_____

What you are reading this week: _____

_____

What you are listening to this week: _____

_____

Ideas

Week Three: *May*

17 *Monday*

18 *Tuesday*

19 *Wednesday*

20 *Thursday*

Top Three Goals:
    1.
    2.

    3.

21 *Friday*

22 *Saturday*

23 *Sunday*

Additional Notes:

Review + Action Plan Week Three: May

Use this page as you prepare for the week ahead, during Sunday planning time.

What went well last week? _____

_____

What did not go so well? _____

_____

What did you learn? _____

_____

What will you do differently this week because of what you learned? _____

_____

Projects to work on this week and top three actions to take with each:

    (write each activity into your schedule right now)

      1.

      2.

      3.

Prospects to follow up on: _____

_____

Obstacles that could get in your way: _____

_____

Solutions for facing possible obstacles: _____

_____

_____

Three things you are most grateful for:

      1.

      2.

      3.

What is your mantra or affirmation for the week? *(write it and repeat it often!)* _____

_____

_____

What you are reading this week: _____

_____

What you are listening to this week: _____

Ideas

Week **Four:** *May*

24 *Monday*

25 *Tuesday*

26 *Wednesday*

27 *Thursday*

Top Three Goals:
1.
2.
3.

28 *Friday*

29 *Saturday*

30 *Sunday*

Additional Notes:

Review + Action Plan Week Four: May

Use this page as you prepare for the week ahead, during Sunday planning time.

What went well last week? _____

_____

What did not go so well? _____

_____

What did you learn? _____

_____

What will you do differently this week because of what you learned? _____

_____

Projects to work on this week and top three actions to take with each:

   (write each activity into your schedule right now)

   1.

   2.

   3.

Prospects to follow up on: _____

_____

Obstacles that could get in your way: _____

_____

Solutions for facing possible obstacles: _____

_____

_____

Three things you are most grateful for:

   1.

   2.

   3.

What is your mantra or affirmation for the week? *(write it and repeat it often!)* _____

_____

_____

What you are reading this week: _____

_____

What you are listening to this week: _____

_____

Monthly Reflection: *May*

What went well?

_____
_____
_____
_____

What are you most proud of?

_____
_____
_____
_____

What goals did you achieve?

_____
_____
_____
_____

What did not go so well?

_____
_____
_____
_____

What did you learn?

_____
_____
_____
_____

What will you do differently based on what you have learned?

_____
_____
_____

Total income: _____

Your Top Goals: *June*

Monthly Financial Plan

Projected income: _____

Projected or possible income sources: _____

This month's coaching clients: _____

This month's prospects, or people to follow up with: _____

Total coaching slots to be filled: _____

Actual slots filled at the beginning of the month: _____

This month's business expenses: _____

This month's $$ to tax account: _____

This month's projected profit (income - taxes and business expenses): _____

Monthly Plan: *June*

Who will you reach out to for help? _____

_____

Who will hold you accountable? _____

_____

In what resources will you invest? _____

_____

What is your income goal, and where will it come from? (names and events) _____

_____

_____

Who are your top 3 prospects for future business?

    1.

    2.

    3.

What are you creating now to come to fruition over the next 90 days? _____

_____

How will you stay visible through networking? *(people, events- how? What? When?)* _____

_____

_____

What results do you intend to get through these networking actions? _____

_____

_____

How many people do you intend to add to your database this month? _____

Consult your plan you made for the year to keep on track.

June Monthly *Plan* Continued

What is your theme for the month? _____

Monthly (or more often) newsletter:
Use the template for creating your newsletter located under resources (pg. 261) to guide you. There are 12 included, so please copy and use (I permit you) if you are doing a more regular newsletter. Mine is weekly as of January 2020, but was monthly for 12 years prior!

Schedule the date or days you will send your newsletter out on your monthly calendar.

Social media plan*: (find clients, increase following) *See the expanded Social Media Plan on page 315 for additional planning guidance!* _____
_____
_____
_____

Where will you post, and how often? _____
_____
_____
_____

What content will you share? *Have a separate notebook for sketching out social media content if necessary.* _____
_____
_____
_____

How often and on what platforms will you go live? *Schedule days, times, and topics into your monthly calendar.* _____
_____
_____
_____

What are your specific goals around your social media actions? _____
_____
_____
_____

Ideas

Monthly **Overview:** *June*

Sunday	Monday	Tuesday	Wednesday
30	31	1	2
6	7	8	9
13	14	15	16
20	21	22	23
27	28	29	30
4	5	6	7

Thursday	Friday	Saturday	Notes
3	4	5	Income goal: _____
			Top three prospects: 1. _____
10	11	12	2. _____
			3. _____
17	18	19	Networking events this month: _____
			_____
24	25	26	_____
			Events to work on this month for the future (90 day out-look):
1	2	3	_____
8	9	10	_____

Week One: *June*

31 *Monday*

1 *Tuesday*

2 *Wednesday*

3 *Thursday*

Top Three Goals:
  1.
  2.
  3.

4 *Friday*

5 *Saturday*

6 *Sunday*

Additional Notes:

Review + Action Plan Week One: June

Use this page as you prepare for the week ahead, during Sunday planning time.

What went well last week? _____

_____

What did not go so well? _____

_____

What did you learn? _____

_____

What will you do differently this week because of what you learned? _____

_____

Projects to work on this week and top three actions to take with each:

(write each activity into your schedule right now)

    1.

    2.

    3.

Prospects to follow up on: _____

_____

Obstacles that could get in your way: _____

_____

Solutions for facing possible obstacles: _____

_____

_____

Three things you are most grateful for:

    1.

    2.

    3.

What is your mantra or affirmation for the week? *(write it and repeat it often!)* _____

_____

_____

What you are reading this week: _____

_____

What you are listening to this week: _____

Ideas

Week Two: *June*

7 *Monday*

8 *Tuesday*

9 *Wednesday*

10 *Thursday*

Top Three Goals:

1.

2.

3.

11 *Friday*

12 *Saturday*

13 *Sunday*

Additional Notes:

Review + Action Plan Week Two: June

Use this page as you prepare for the week ahead, during Sunday planning time.

What went well last week? _____

_____

What did not go so well? _____

_____

What did you learn? _____

_____

What will you do differently this week because of what you learned? _____

_____

Projects to work on this week and top three actions to take with each:

    (write each activity into your schedule right now)

      1.

      2.

      3.

Prospects to follow up on: _____

_____

Obstacles that could get in your way: _____

_____

Solutions for facing possible obstacles: _____

_____

_____

Three things you are most grateful for:

      1.

      2.

      3.

What is your mantra or affirmation for the week? *(write it and repeat it often!)* _____

_____

_____

What you are reading this week: _____

_____

What you are listening to this week: _____

146 _____

Ideas

Week Three: *June*

14 *Monday*

15 *Tuesday*

16 *Wednesday*

17 *Thursday*

Top Three Goals:
1.
2.
3.

18 *Friday*

19 *Saturday*

20 *Sunday*

Additional Notes:

Review + Action Plan

Use this page as you prepare for the week ahead, during Sunday planning time.

What went well last week? _____

_____

What did not go so well? _____

_____

What did you learn? _____

_____

What will you do differently this week because of what you learned? _____

_____

Projects to work on this week and top three actions to take with each:
   (write each activity into your schedule right now)
   1.
   2.
   3.

Prospects to follow up on: _____

_____

Obstacles that could get in your way: _____

_____

Solutions for facing possible obstacles: _____

_____

_____

Three things you are most grateful for:
   1.
   2.
   3.

What is your mantra or affirmation for the week? *(write it and repeat it often!)* _____

_____

_____

What you are reading this week: _____

_____

What you are listening to this week: _____

_____

Ideas

Week **Four:** *June*

21 *Monday*

22 *Tuesday*

23 *Wednesday*

24 *Thursday*

Top Three Goals:
1.
2.
3.

25 *Friday*

26 *Saturday*

27 *Sunday*

Additional Notes:

Review + Action Plan Week Four: June

Use this page as you prepare for the week ahead, during Sunday planning time.

What went well last week? _____

_____

What did not go so well? _____

_____

What did you learn? _____

_____

What will you do differently this week because of what you learned? _____

_____

Projects to work on this week and top three actions to take with each:
>   *(write each activity into your schedule right now)*
>   1.
>   2.
>   3.

Prospects to follow up on: _____

_____

Obstacles that could get in your way: _____

_____

Solutions for facing possible obstacles: _____

_____

_____

Three things you are most grateful for:
>   1.
>   2.
>   3.

What is your mantra or affirmation for the week? *(write it and repeat it often!)* _____

_____

_____

What you are reading this week: _____

_____

What you are listening to this week: _____

Monthly Reflection: *June*

It's time for your SECOND QUARTER review! Please flip to page 312 to get it done!

What went well?

_____
_____
_____
_____

What are you most proud of?

_____
_____
_____
_____
_____

What goals did you achieve?

_____
_____
_____
_____
_____

What did not go so well?

_____
_____
_____
_____
_____

What did you learn?

_____
_____
_____
_____
_____

What will you do differently based on what you have learned?

_____
_____
_____
_____

Total income: _____   155

Your Top Goals: *July*

Monthly Financial Plan

Projected income: _____

Projected or possible income sources: _____

This month's coaching clients: _____

This month's prospects, or people to follow up with: _____

Total coaching slots to be filled: _____

Actual slots filled at the beginning of the month: _____

This month's business expenses: _____

This month's $$ to tax account: _____

This month's projected profit (income - taxes and business expenses): _____

Monthly Plan: *July*

Who will you reach out to for help? _____

_____

Who will hold you accountable? _____

_____

In what resources will you invest? _____

_____

What is your income goal, and where will it come from? (names and events) _____

_____

_____

Who are your top 3 prospects for future business?

    1.

    2.

    3.

What are you creating now to come to fruition over the next 90 days? _____

_____

_____

How will you stay visible through networking? *(people, events- how? What? When?)* _____

_____

_____

What results do you intend to get through these networking actions? _____

_____

_____

How many people do you intend to add to your database this month? _____

Consult your plan you made for the year to keep on track.

July Monthly **Plan** Continued

What is your theme for the month? _____

Monthly (or more often) newsletter:

Use the template for creating your newsletter located under resources (pg. 261) to guide you. There are 12 included, so please copy and use (I permit you) if you are doing a more regular newsletter. Mine is weekly as of January 2020, but was monthly for 12 years prior!

Schedule the date or days you will send your newsletter out on your monthly calendar.

Social media plan*: (find clients, increase following) *See the expanded Social Media Plan on page 315 for additional planning guidance!* _____

_____

_____

_____

Where will you post, and how often? _____

_____

_____

_____

What content will you share? *Have a separate notebook for sketching out social media content if necessary.* _____

_____

_____

_____

How often and on what platforms will you go live? *Schedule days, times, and topics into your monthly calendar.* _____

_____

_____

_____

What are your specific goals around your social media actions? _____

_____

_____

_____

Ideas

Monthly Overview: *July*

Sunday	Monday	Tuesday	Wednesday
27	28	29	30
4	5	6	7
11	12	13	14
18	19	20	21
25	26	27	28

160

Thursday	Friday	Saturday	Notes
1	2	3	Income goal: _____ Top three prospects: 1. _____
8	9	10	2. _____ 3.
15	16	17	Networking events this month: _____ _____
22	23	24	_____ _____ _____ _____ Events to work on
29	30	31	this month for the future (90 day outlook): _____ _____ _____
			_____ _____

Week One: *July*

28 *Monday*

29 *Tuesday*

30 *Wednesday*

1 *Thursday*

Top Three Goals:
1.
2.
3.

2 *Friday*

3 *Saturday*

4 *Sunday*

Additional Notes:

Review + Action Plan

Use this page as you prepare for the week ahead, during Sunday planning time.

What went well last week? _____
_____

What did not go so well? _____
_____

What did you learn? _____
_____

What will you do differently this week because of what you learned? _____
_____

Projects to work on this week and top three actions to take with each:
(write each activity into your schedule right now)

    1.

    2.

    3.

Prospects to follow up on: _____
_____

Obstacles that could get in your way: _____
_____

Solutions for facing possible obstacles: _____
_____
_____

Three things you are most grateful for:

    1.

    2.

    3.

What is your mantra or affirmation for the week? *(write it and repeat it often!)* _____
_____
_____

What you are reading this week: _____
_____

What you are listening to this week: _____

_____

Ideas

Week Two: *July*

5 *Monday*

6 *Tuesday*

7 *Wednesday*

8 *Thursday*

Top Three Goals:

1.

2.

3.

9 *Friday*

10 *Saturday*

11 *Sunday*

Additional Notes:

Review + Action Plan

Use this page as you prepare for the week ahead, during Sunday planning time.

What went well last week? _____

_____

What did not go so well? _____

_____

What did you learn? _____

_____

What will you do differently this week because of what you learned? _____

_____

Projects to work on this week and top three actions to take with each:

    (write each activity into your schedule right now)

    1.

    2.

    3.

Prospects to follow up on: _____

_____

Obstacles that could get in your way: _____

_____

Solutions for facing possible obstacles: _____

_____

_____

Three things you are most grateful for:

    1.

    2.

    3.

What is your mantra or affirmation for the week? *(write it and repeat it often!)* _____

_____

_____

What you are reading this week: _____

_____

What you are listening to this week: _____

Ideas

Week Three: *July*

12 *Monday*

13 *Tuesday*

14 *Wednesday*

15 *Thursday*

Top Three Goals:

1.

2.

3.

16 *Friday*

17 *Saturday*

18 *Sunday*

Additional Notes:

Review + Action Plan

Use this page as you prepare for the week ahead, during Sunday planning time.

What went well last week? _____

_____

What did not go so well? _____

_____

What did you learn? _____

_____

What will you do differently this week because of what you learned? _____

_____

Projects to work on this week and top three actions to take with each:
> *(write each activity into your schedule right now)*
>
> 1.
> 2.
> 3.

Prospects to follow up on: _____

_____

Obstacles that could get in your way: _____

_____

Solutions for facing possible obstacles: _____

_____

_____

Three things you are most grateful for:
> 1.
> 2.
> 3.

What is your mantra or affirmation for the week? *(write it and repeat it often!)* _____

_____

_____

What you are reading this week: _____

_____

What you are listening to this week: _____

172 _____

Ideas

Week **Four:** *July*

19 *Monday*

20 *Tuesday*

21 *Wednesday*

22 *Thursday*

Top Three Goals:
1.
2.
3.

23 *Friday*

24 *Saturday*

25 *Sunday*

Additional Notes:

Review + Action Plan Week Four: July

Use this page as you prepare for the week ahead, during Sunday planning time.

What went well last week? _____

_____

What did not go so well? _____

_____

What did you learn? _____

_____

What will you do differently this week because of what you learned? _____

_____

Projects to work on this week and top three actions to take with each:
    (write each activity into your schedule right now)
       1.
       2.
       3.

Prospects to follow up on: _____

_____

Obstacles that could get in your way: _____

_____

Solutions for facing possible obstacles: _____

_____

_____

Three things you are most grateful for:
       1.
       2.
       3.

What is your mantra or affirmation for the week? *(write it and repeat it often!)* _____

_____

_____

What you are reading this week: _____

_____

What you are listening to this week: _____

Ideas

Week **Five:** *July*

26 *Monday*

27 *Tuesday*

28 *Wednesday*

29 *Thursday*

Top Three Goals:
1.
2.
3.

30 *Friday*

31 *Saturday*

1 *Sunday*

Additional Notes:

Review + Action Plan

Use this page as you prepare for the week ahead, during Sunday planning time.

What went well last week? _____

_____

What did not go so well? _____

_____

What did you learn? _____

_____

What will you do differently this week because of what you learned? _____

_____

Projects to work on this week and top three actions to take with each:

    (write each activity into your schedule right now)

      1.

      2.

      3.

Prospects to follow up on: _____

_____

Obstacles that could get in your way: _____

_____

Solutions for facing possible obstacles: _____

_____

_____

Three things you are most grateful for:

      1.

      2.

      3.

What is your mantra or affirmation for the week? *(write it and repeat it often!)* _____

_____

_____

What you are reading this week: _____

_____

What you are listening to this week:_____

_____

Ideas

"Find what brings you joy and spend some time doing it everyday."
Kimberly DuBrul

Monthly Reflection: *July*

What went well?

_____
_____
_____
_____

What are you most proud of?

_____
_____
_____
_____
_____

What goals did you achieve?

_____
_____
_____
_____
_____

What did not go so well?

_____
_____
_____
_____

What did you learn?

_____
_____
_____
_____

What will you do differently based on what you have learned?

_____
_____
_____
_____

Total income: _____

Your Top Goals: *August*

Monthly Financial Plan

Projected income: _____

Projected or possible income sources: _____

This month's coaching clients: _____

This month's prospects, or people to follow up with: _____

Total coaching slots to be filled: _____

Actual slots filled at the beginning of the month: _____

This month's business expenses: _____

This month's $$ to tax account: _____

This month's projected profit (income - taxes and business expenses): _____ 183

Monthly Plan: *August*

Who will you reach out to for help? _____

_____

Who will hold you accountable? _____

_____

In what resources will you invest? _____

_____

What is your income goal, and where will it come from? (names and events) _____

_____

_____

Who are your top 3 prospects for future business?

     1.

     2.

     3.

What are you creating now to come to fruition over the next 90 days? _____

_____

_____

How will you stay visible through networking? *(people, events- how? What? When?)* _____

_____

_____

What results do you intend to get through these networking actions? _____

_____

_____

How many people do you intend to add to your database this month? _____

Consult your plan you made for the year to keep on track.

August Monthly *Plan* Continued

What is your theme for the month? _____

Monthly (or more often) newsletter:
Use the template for creating your newsletter located under resources (pg. 261) to guide you. There are 12 included, so please copy and use (I permit you) if you are doing a more regular newsletter. Mine is weekly as of January 2020, but was monthly for 12 years prior!

Schedule the date or days you will send your newsletter out on your monthly calendar.

Social media plan*: (find clients, increase following) *See the expanded Social Media Plan on page 315 for additional planning guidance!* _____
_____
_____
_____

Where will you post, and how often? _____
_____
_____

What content will you share? *Have a separate notebook for sketching out social media content if necessary:* _____
_____
_____

How often and on what platforms will you go live? *Schedule days, times, and topics into your monthly calendar:* _____
_____
_____

What are your specific goals around your social media actions? _____
_____
_____
_____

Monthly **Overview:** *August*

Sunday	Monday	Tuesday	Wednesday
1	2	3	4
8	9	10	11
15	16	17	18
22	23	24	25
29	30	31	

Thursday	Friday	Saturday	Notes
5	6	7	Income goal: Top three prospects: 1.
12	13	14	2. 3.
19	20	21	Networking events this month:
26	27	28	
			Events to work on this month for the future (90 day outlook):

Week One: *August*

2 *Monday*

3 *Tuesday*

4 *Wednesday*

5 *Thursday*

Top Three Goals:

1.

2.

3.

6 *Friday*

7 *Saturday*

8 *Sunday*

Additional Notes:

Review + Action Plan

Use this page as you prepare for the week ahead, during Sunday planning time.

What went well last week? _____

_____

What did not go so well? _____

_____

What did you learn? _____

_____

What will you do differently this week because of what you learned? _____

_____

Projects to work on this week and top three actions to take with each:
> *(write each activity into your schedule right now)*

    1.

    2.

    3.

Prospects to follow up on: _____

_____

Obstacles that could get in your way: _____

_____

Solutions for facing possible obstacles: _____

_____

_____

Three things you are most grateful for:

    1.

    2.

    3.

What is your mantra or affirmation for the week? *(write it and repeat it often!)* _____

_____

_____

What you are reading this week: _____

_____

What you are listening to this week: _____

_____

Ideas

Week **Two**: *August*

9 *Monday*

10 *Tuesday*

11 *Wednesday*

12 *Thursday*

Top Three Goals:
1.
2.
192 3.

13 *Friday*

14 *Saturday*

15 *Sunday*

Additional Notes:

Review + Action Plan

Use this page as you prepare for the week ahead, during Sunday planning time.

What went well last week? _____

_____

What did not go so well? _____

_____

What did you learn? _____

_____

What will you do differently this week because of what you learned? _____

_____

Projects to work on this week and top three actions to take with each:

    (write each activity into your schedule right now)

    1.

    2.

    3.

Prospects to follow up on: _____

_____

Obstacles that could get in your way: _____

_____

Solutions for facing possible obstacles: _____

_____

_____

Three things you are most grateful for:

    1.

    2.

    3.

What is your mantra or affirmation for the week? *(write it and repeat it often!)* _____

_____

What you are reading this week: _____

_____

What you are listening to this week: _____

Ideas

Week Three: *August*

16 *Monday*

17 *Tuesday*

18 *Wednesday*

19 *Thursday*

Top Three Goals:

1.
2.
3.

20 *Friday*

21 *Saturday*

22 *Sunday*

Additional Notes:

Review + Action Plan

Use this page as you prepare for the week ahead, during Sunday planning time.

What went well last week? _____

_____

What did not go so well? _____

_____

What did you learn? _____

_____

What will you do differently this week because of what you learned? _____

_____

Projects to work on this week and top three actions to take with each:

    (write each activity into your schedule right now)

       1.

       2.

       3.

Prospects to follow up on: _____

_____

Obstacles that could get in your way: _____

_____

Solutions for facing possible obstacles: _____

_____

_____

Three things you are most grateful for:

       1.

       2.

       3.

What is your mantra or affirmation for the week? *(write it and repeat it often!)* _____

_____

_____

What you are reading this week: _____

_____

What you are listening to this week: _____

_____

Ideas

Week **Four:** *August*

23 *Monday*

24 *Tuesday*

25 *Wednesday*

26 *Thursday*

Top Three Goals:

    1.

    2.

    3.

27 *Friday*

28 *Saturday*

29 *Sunday*

Additional Notes:

Review + Action Plan Week Four: August

Use this page as you prepare for the week ahead, during Sunday planning time.

What went well last week? _____
_____

What did not go so well? _____
_____

What did you learn? _____
_____

What will you do differently this week because of what you learned? _____
_____

Projects to work on this week and top three actions to take with each:
    (write each activity into your schedule right now)
        1.
        2.
        3.

Prospects to follow up on: _____
_____

Obstacles that could get in your way: _____
_____

Solutions for facing possible obstacles: _____
_____
_____

Three things you are most grateful for:
        1.
        2.
        3.

What is your mantra or affirmation for the week? *(write it and repeat it often!)* _____
_____
_____

What you are reading this week: _____
_____

What you are listening to this week: _____

Monthly **Reflection:** *August*

What went well?

_____
_____
_____
_____

What are you most proud of?

_____
_____
_____
_____
_____

What goals did you achieve?

_____
_____
_____
_____
_____

What did not go so well?

_____
_____
_____
_____

What did you learn?

_____
_____
_____
_____

What will you do differently based on what you have learned?

_____
_____
_____

Total income: _____

Your Top Goals: *September*

Monthly Financial Plan

Projected income: _____

Projected or possible income sources: _____

This month's coaching clients: _____

This month's prospects, or people to follow up with: _____

Total coaching slots to be filled: _____

Actual slots filled at the beginning of the month: _____

This month's business expenses: _____

This month's $$ to tax account: _____

This month's projected profit (income - taxes and business expenses): _____

Monthly Plan: *September*

Who will you reach out to for help? _____

_____

_____

Who will hold you accountable? _____

_____

_____

In what resources will you invest? _____

_____

_____

What is your income goal, and where will it come from? (names and events) _____

_____

_____

_____

Who are your top 3 prospects for future business?

     1.

     2.

     3.

What are you creating now to come to fruition over the next 90 days? _____

_____

_____

_____

How will you stay visible through networking? *(people, events- how? What? When?)* _____

_____

_____

_____

What results do you intend to get through these networking actions? _____

_____

_____

_____

How many people do you intend to add to your database this month? _____

Consult your plan you made for the year to keep on track.

September Monthly *Plan* Continued

What is your theme for the month? _____

Monthly (or more often) newsletter:
Use the template for creating your newsletter located under resources (pg. 261) to guide you. There are 12 included, so please copy and use (I permit you) if you are doing a more regular newsletter. Mine is weekly as of January 2020, but was monthly for 12 years prior!

Schedule the date or days you will send your newsletter out on your monthly calendar.

Social media plan*: (find clients, increase following) *See the expanded Social Media Plan on page 315 for additional planning guidance!* _____
_____
_____
_____

Where will you post, and how often? _____
_____
_____
_____

What content will you share? *Have a separate notebook for sketching out social media content if necessary.* _____
_____
_____
_____

How often and on what platforms will you go live? *Schedule days, times, and topics into your monthly calendar.* _____
_____
_____
_____

What are your specific goals around your social media actions? _____
_____
_____
_____

Ideas

Monthly Overview: *September*

Monthly Theme: _____

Sunday	Monday	Tuesday	Wednesday
29	30	31	1
5	6	7	8
12	13	14	15
19	20	21	22
26	27	28	29

Thursday	Friday	Saturday	Notes
2	3	4	Income goal: _____
9	10	11	Top three prospects: 1. _____ 2. _____ 3.
16	17	18	Networking events this month: _____ _____ _____
23	24	25	_____ _____ _____
30			Events to work on this month for the future (90 day outlook): _____ _____ _____
			_____ _____ _____

Week **One:** *September*

30 *Monday*

31 *Tuesday*

1 *Wednesday*

2 *Thursday*

Top Three Goals:
1.
2.
3.

3 *Friday*

4 *Saturday*

5 *Sunday*

Additional Notes:

Review + Action Plan

Use this page as you prepare for the week ahead, during Sunday planning time.

What went well last week? _____

_____

What did not go so well? _____

_____

What did you learn? _____

_____

What will you do differently this week because of what you learned? _____

_____

Projects to work on this week and top three actions to take with each:

    (write each activity into your schedule right now)

    1.

    2.

    3.

Prospects to follow up on: _____

_____

Obstacles that could get in your way: _____

_____

Solutions for facing possible obstacles: _____

_____

_____

Three things you are most grateful for:

    1.

    2.

    3.

What is your mantra or affirmation for the week? *(write it and repeat it often!)* _____

_____

What you are reading this week: _____

_____

What you are listening to this week: _____

_____

Ideas

Week **Two**: *September*

6 *Monday*

7 *Tuesday*

8 *Wednesday*

9 *Thursday*

Top Three Goals:

1.
2.
3.

10 *Friday*

11 *Saturday*

12 *Sunday*

Additional Notes:

Review + Action Plan Week Two: September

Use this page as you prepare for the week ahead, during Sunday planning time.

What went well last week? _____

_____

What did not go so well? _____

_____

What did you learn? _____

_____

What will you do differently this week because of what you learned? _____

_____

Projects to work on this week and top three actions to take with each:

    (write each activity into your schedule right now)

    1.

    2.

    3.

Prospects to follow up on: _____

_____

Obstacles that could get in your way: _____

_____

Solutions for facing possible obstacles: _____

_____

_____

Three things you are most grateful for:

    1.

    2.

    3.

What is your mantra or affirmation for the week? *(write it and repeat it often!)* _____

_____

_____

What you are reading this week: _____

_____

What you are listening to this week: _____

_____

Ideas

Week **Three:** *September*

13 *Monday*

14 *Tuesday*

15 *Wednesday*

16 *Thursday*

Top Three Goals:

     1.

     2.

     3.

17 *Friday*

18 *Saturday*

19 *Sunday*

Additional Notes:

Review + Action Plan

Use this page as you prepare for the week ahead, during Sunday planning time.

What went well last week? _____

_____

What did not go so well? _____

_____

What did you learn? _____

_____

What will you do differently this week because of what you learned? _____

_____

Projects to work on this week and top three actions to take with each:

    (write each activity into your schedule right now)

    1.

    2.

    3.

Prospects to follow up on: _____

_____

Obstacles that could get in your way: _____

_____

Solutions for facing possible obstacles: _____

_____

_____

Three things you are most grateful for:

    1.

    2.

    3.

What is your mantra or affirmation for the week? *(write it and repeat it often!)* _____

_____

_____

What you are reading this week: _____

_____

What you are listening to this week: _____

220 _____

Ideas

Week **Four:** *September*

20 *Monday*

21 *Tuesday*

22 *Wednesday*

23 *Thursday*

Top Three Goals:

1.

2.

3.

24 *Friday*

25 *Saturday*

26 *Sunday*

Additional Notes:

Review + Action Plan

Use this page as you prepare for the week ahead, during Sunday planning time.

What went well last week? _____
_____

What did not go so well? _____
_____

What did you learn? _____
_____

What will you do differently this week because of what you learned? _____
_____

Projects to work on this week and top three actions to take with each:
  (write each activity into your schedule right now)
    1.
    2.
    3.

Prospects to follow up on: _____
_____

Obstacles that could get in your way: _____
_____

Solutions for facing possible obstacles: _____
_____
_____

Three things you are most grateful for:
    1.
    2.
    3.

What is your mantra or affirmation for the week? *(write it and repeat it often!)* _____
_____
_____

What you are reading this week: _____
_____

What you are listening to this week: _____

_____

Ideas

Week **Five:** *September*

27 *Monday*

28 *Tuesday*

29 *Wednesday*

30 *Thursday*

Top Three Goals:

    1.

    2.

  3.

1 *Friday*
2 *Saturday*
3 *Sunday*

Additional Notes:

Review + Action Plan

Use this page as you prepare for the week ahead, during Sunday planning time.

What went well last week? _____

_____

What did not go so well? _____

_____

What did you learn? _____

_____

What will you do differently this week because of what you learned? _____

_____

Projects to work on this week and top three actions to take with each:

    (write each activity into your schedule right now)

        1.

        2.

        3.

Prospects to follow up on: _____

_____

Obstacles that could get in your way: _____

_____

Solutions for facing possible obstacles: _____

_____

_____

Three things you are most grateful for:

        1.

        2.

        3.

What is your mantra or affirmation for the week? *(write it and repeat it often!)* _____

_____

_____

What you are reading this week: _____

_____

What you are listening to this week: _____

_____

Ideas

"Control your schedule or someone else will!"
Kimberly DuBrul

Monthly Reflection: *September*

It's time for your THIRD QUARTER review! Please flip to page 313 to get it done!

What went well?

_____

_____

_____

_____

What are you most proud of?

_____

_____

_____

_____

What goals did you achieve?

_____

_____

_____

_____

What did not go so well?

_____

_____

_____

_____

What did you learn?

_____

_____

_____

_____

What will you do differently based on what you have learned?

_____

_____

_____

230   Total income: _____

Your Top Goals: *October*

Monthly Financial Plan

Projected income: _____

Projected or possible income sources: _____

This month's coaching clients: _____

This month's prospects, or people to follow up with: _____

Total coaching slots to be filled: _____

Actual slots filled at the beginning of the month: _____

This month's business expenses: _____

This month's $$ to tax account: _____

This month's projected profit (income - taxes and business expenses): _____

Monthly Plan: *October*

Who will you reach out to for help? _____

_____

_____

Who will hold you accountable? _____

_____

_____

In what resources will you invest? _____

_____

_____

What is your income goal, and where will it come from? (names and events) _____

_____

_____

_____

Who are your top 3 prospects for future business?

     1.

     2.

     3.

What are you creating now to come to fruition over the next 90 days? _____

_____

_____

_____

How will you stay visible through networking? *(people, events- how? What? When?)* _____

_____

_____

_____

What results do you intend to get through these networking actions? _____

_____

_____

_____

How many people do you intend to add to your database this month? _____

Consult your plan you made for the year to keep on track.

October Monthly *Plan* Continued

What is your theme for the month? _____

Monthly (or more often) newsletter:
Use the template for creating your newsletter located under resources (pg. 261) to guide you.
There are 12 included, so please copy and use (I permit you) if you are doing a more regular
newsletter. Mine is weekly as of January 2020, but was monthly for 12 years prior!

Schedule the date or days you will send your newsletter out on your monthly calendar.

Social media plan*: (find clients, increase following) *See the expanded Social Media Plan on*
page 267 for additional planning guidance! _____
_____
_____
_____

Where will you post, and how often? _____
_____
_____
_____

What content will you share? *Have a separate notebook for sketching out social media content if*
necessary: _____
_____
_____
_____

How often and on what platforms will you go live? *Schedule days, times, and topics into your*
monthly calendar. _____
_____
_____
_____

What are your specific goals around your social media actions? _____
_____
_____
_____

Monthly Overview: *October*

Monthly Theme: _____

Sunday	Monday	Tuesday	Wednesday
26	27	28	29
3	4	5	6
10	11	12	13
17	18	19	20
24	25	26	27
31			

Thursday	Friday	Saturday	Notes
31	1	2	Income goal: _____ Top three prospects: 1. _____
7	8	9	2. _____ 3. _____
14	15	16	Networking events this month: _____ _____ _____
21	22	23	_____ _____ _____ Events to work on this month for the future (90 day out-
28	29	30	look): _____ _____ _____
4	5	6	_____ _____ _____

Week **One**: *October*

27 *Monday*

28 *Tuesday*

29 *Wednesday*

30 *Thursday*

Top Three Goals:

1.

2.

3.

1 *Friday*

2 *Saturday*

3 *Sunday*

Additional Notes:

Review + Action Plan

Use this page as you prepare for the week ahead, during Sunday planning time.

What went well last week? _____

_____

What did not go so well? _____

_____

What did you learn? _____

_____

What will you do differently this week because of what you learned? _____

_____

Projects to work on this week and top three actions to take with each:

    (write each activity into your schedule right now)

      1.

      2.

      3.

Prospects to follow up on: _____

_____

Obstacles that could get in your way: _____

_____

Solutions for facing possible obstacles: _____

_____

_____

Three things you are most grateful for:

      1.

      2.

      3.

What is your mantra or affirmation for the week? *(write it and repeat it often!)* _____

_____

_____

What you are reading this week: _____

_____

What you are listening to this week: _____

_____

Ideas

Week **Two**: *October*

4 *Monday*

5 *Tuesday*

6 *Wednesday*

7 *Thursday*

Top Three Goals:

1.

2.

3.

8 *Friday*

9 *Saturday*

10 *Sunday*

Additional Notes:

Review + Action Plan

Use this page as you prepare for the week ahead, during Sunday planning time.

What went well last week? _____

_____

What did not go so well? _____

_____

What did you learn? _____

_____

What will you do differently this week because of what you learned? _____

_____

Projects to work on this week and top three actions to take with each:

    (write each activity into your schedule right now)

      1.

      2.

      3.

Prospects to follow up on: _____

_____

Obstacles that could get in your way: _____

_____

Solutions for facing possible obstacles: _____

_____

_____

Three things you are most grateful for:

      1.

      2.

      3.

What is your mantra or affirmation for the week? *(write it and repeat it often!)* _____

_____

_____

What you are reading this week: _____

_____

What you are listening to this week: _____

_____

Ideas

Week Three: *October*

11 *Monday*

12 *Tuesday*

13 *Wednesday*

14 *Thursday*

Top Three Goals:

1.

2.

244   3.

15 *Friday*

16 *Saturday*

17 *Sunday*

Additional Notes:

Review + Action Plan Week Three: October

Use this page as you prepare for the week ahead, during Sunday planning time.

What went well last week? _____
_____

What did not go so well? _____
_____

What did you learn? _____
_____

What will you do differently this week because of what you learned? _____
_____

Projects to work on this week and top three actions to take with each:

    (write each activity into your schedule right now)

       1.

       2.

       3.

Prospects to follow up on: _____
_____

Obstacles that could get in your way: _____
_____

Solutions for facing possible obstacles: _____
_____
_____

Three things you are most grateful for:

       1.

       2.

       3.

What is your mantra or affirmation for the week? *(write it and repeat it often!)* _____
_____
_____

What you are reading this week: _____
_____

What you are listening to this week: _____

Ideas

Week **Four**: *October*

18 *Monday*

19 *Tuesday*

20 *Wednesday*

21 *Thursday*

Top Three Goals:
1.
2.

3.

22 *Friday*

23 *Saturday*

24 *Sunday*

Additional Notes:

Review + Action Plan Week Four: October

Use this page as you prepare for the week ahead, during Sunday planning time.

What went well last week? _____
_____

What did not go so well? _____
_____

What did you learn? _____
_____

What will you do differently this week because of what you learned? ____
_____

Projects to work on this week and top three actions to take with each:
    (write each activity into your schedule right now)
    1.
    2.
    3.

Prospects to follow up on: _____
_____

Obstacles that could get in your way: _____
_____

Solutions for facing possible obstacles: _____
_____
_____

Three things you are most grateful for:
    1.
    2.
    3.

What is your mantra or affirmation for the week? *(write it and repeat it often!)* _____
_____
_____

What you are reading this week: _____
_____

What you are listening to this week: _____

Ideas

Week **Five:** *October*

25 *Monday*

26 *Tuesday*

27 *Wednesday*

Top Three Goals:
1.
2.

3.

29 *Friday*

30 *Saturday*

31 *Sunday*

Additional Notes:

Review + Action Plan Week Five: October

Use this page as you prepare for the week ahead, during Sunday planning time.

What went well last week? _____

_____

What did not go so well? _____

_____

What did you learn? _____

_____

What will you do differently this week because of what you learned? _____

_____

Projects to work on this week and top three actions to take with each:

    (write each activity into your schedule right now)

    1.

    2.

    3.

Prospects to follow up on: _____

_____

Obstacles that could get in your way: _____

_____

Solutions for facing possible obstacles: _____

_____

_____

Three things you are most grateful for:

    1.

    2.

    3.

What is your mantra or affirmation for the week? *(write it and repeat it often!)* _____

_____

What you are reading this week: _____

_____

What you are listening to this week: _____

Ideas

"Spend more time thinking about what you DO want and less time thinking about what you don't have." Kimberly DuBrul

Monthly Reflection: *October*

What went well?

_____
_____
_____
_____

What are you most proud of?

_____
_____
_____
_____
_____

What goals did you achieve?

_____
_____
_____
_____
_____

What did not go so well?

_____
_____
_____
_____
_____

What did you learn?

_____
_____
_____
_____
_____

What will you do differently based on what you have learned?

_____
_____
_____
_____

Total income: _____

Your Top Goals: *November*

Monthly Financial Plan

Projected income: _____

Projected or possible income sources: _____

This month's coaching clients: _____

This month's prospects, or people to follow up with: _____

Total coaching slots to be filled: _____

Actual slots filled at the beginning of the month: _____

This month's business expenses: _____

This month's $$ to tax account: _____

This month's projected profit (income - taxes and business expenses): _____ 257

Monthly Plan: *November*

Who will you reach out to for help? _____

_____

_____

Who will hold you accountable? _____

_____

_____

In what resources will you invest? _____

_____

_____

What is your income goal, and where will it come from? (names and events) _____

_____

_____

_____

Who are your top 3 prospects for future business?

     1.

     2.

     3.

What are you creating now to come to fruition over the next 90 days? _____

_____

_____

_____

How will you stay visible through networking? *(people, events- how? What? When?)* _____

_____

_____

_____

What results do you intend to get through these networking actions? _____

_____

_____

_____

How many people do you intend to add to your database this month? _____

Consult your plan you made for the year to keep on track.

November Monthly **Plan** Continued

What is your theme for the month? _____

Monthly (or more often) newsletter:

Use the template for creating your newsletter located under resources (pg. 261) to guide you. There are 12 included, so please copy and use (I permit you) if you are doing a more regular newsletter. Mine is weekly as of January 2020, but was monthly for 12 years prior!

Schedule the date or days you will send your newsletter out on your monthly calendar.

Social media plan*: (find clients, increase following) **See the expanded Social Media Plan on page 315 for additional planning guidance!* _____

_____

_____

_____

Where will you post, and how often? _____

_____

_____

What content will you share? *Have a separate notebook for sketching out social media content if necessary.* _____

_____

_____

_____

How often and on what platforms will you go live? *Schedule days, times, and topics into your monthly calendar.* _____

_____

_____

_____

What are your specific goals around your social media actions? _____

_____

_____

_____

Monthly Overview: *November*

Sunday	Monday	Tuesday	Wednesday
31	1	2	3
7	8	9	10
14	15	16	17
21	22	23	24
28	29	30	

Thursday	Friday	Saturday	Notes
4	5	6	Income goal: _____
11	12	13	Top three prospects: 1. _____ 2. _____ 3.
18	19	20	Networking events this month: _____ _____ _____
25	26	27	_____ _____ _____ Events to work on this month for the future (90 day outlook):
			_____ _____ _____
			_____ _____ _____

Week **One**: *November*

1 *Monday*

2 *Tuesday*

3 *Wednesday*

4 *Thursday*

Top Three Goals:

1.

2.

3.

5 *Friday*

6 *Saturday*

7 *Sunday*

Additional Notes:

Review + Action Plan

Use this page as you prepare for the week ahead, during Sunday planning time.

What went well last week? _____
_____

What did not go so well? _____
_____

What did you learn? _____
_____

What will you do differently this week because of what you learned? _____
_____

Projects to work on this week and top three actions to take with each:
   (write each activity into your schedule right now)
      1.
      2.
      3.

Prospects to follow up on: _____
_____

Obstacles that could get in your way: _____
_____

Solutions for facing possible obstacles: _____
_____
_____

Three things you are most grateful for:
      1.
      2.
      3.

What is your mantra or affirmation for the week? *(write it and repeat it often!)* _____
_____
_____

What you are reading this week: _____
_____

What you are listening to this week: _____

_____

Ideas

Week **Two**: *November*

8 *Monday*

9 *Tuesday*

10 *Wednesday*

11 *Thursday*

Top Three Goals:

1.

2.

3.

12 *Friday*

13 *Saturday*

14 *Sunday*

Additional Notes:

Review + Action Plan Week Two: November

Use this page as you prepare for the week ahead, during Sunday planning time.

What went well last week? _____
_____

What did not go so well? _____
_____

What did you learn? _____
_____

What will you do differently this week because of what you learned? _____
_____

Projects to work on this week and top three actions to take with each:
> *(write each activity into your schedule right now)*

     1.

     2.

     3.

Prospects to follow up on: _____
_____

Obstacles that could get in your way: _____

Solutions for facing possible obstacles: _____
_____
_____

Three things you are most grateful for:

     1.

     2.

     3.

What is your mantra or affirmation for the week? *(write it and repeat it often!)* _____
_____
_____

What you are reading this week: _____
_____

What you are listening to this week: _____

Ideas

Week **Three:** *November*

15 *Monday*

16 *Tuesday*

17 *Wednesday*

18 *Thursday*

Top Three Goals:

1.

2.

3.

19 *Friday*

20 *Saturday*

21 *Sunday*

Additional Notes:

Review + Action Plan

Use this page as you prepare for the week ahead, during Sunday planning time.

What went well last week? _____

_____

What did not go so well? _____

_____

What did you learn? _____

_____

What will you do differently this week because of what you learned? _____

_____

Projects to work on this week and top three actions to take with each:

    (write each activity into your schedule right now)

    1.

    2.

    3.

Prospects to follow up on: _____

_____

Obstacles that could get in your way: _____

_____

Solutions for facing possible obstacles: _____

_____

_____

Three things you are most grateful for:

    1.

    2.

    3.

What is your mantra or affirmation for the week? *(write it and repeat it often!)* _____

_____

_____

What you are reading this week: _____

_____

What you are listening to this week: _____

_____

Ideas

Week **Four:** *November*

22 *Monday*

23 *Tuesday*

24 *Wednesday*

25 *Thursday*

Top Three Goals:

1.

2.

3.

26 *Friday*

27 *Saturday*

28 *Sunday*

Additional Notes:

Review + Action Plan

Use this page as you prepare for the week ahead, during Sunday planning time.

What went well last week? _____
_____

What did not go so well? _____
_____

What did you learn? _____
_____

What will you do differently this week because of what you learned? _____
_____

Projects to work on this week and top three actions to take with each:

    (write each activity into your schedule right now)

    1.

    2.

    3.

Prospects to follow up on: _____
_____

Obstacles that could get in your way: _____
_____

Solutions for facing possible obstacles: _____
_____
_____

Three things you are most grateful for:

    1.

    2.

    3.

What is your mantra or affirmation for the week? *(write it and repeat it often!)* _____
_____
_____

What you are reading this week: _____
_____

What you are listening to this week: _____

Monthly **Reflection:** *November*

What went well?

_____

_____

_____

_____

_____

What are you most proud of?

_____

_____

_____

_____

_____

_____

What goals did you achieve?

_____

_____

_____

_____

_____

_____

What did not go so well?

_____

_____

_____

_____

_____

_____

What did you learn?

_____

_____

_____

_____

_____

What will you do differently based on what you have learned?

_____

_____

_____

_____

Total income: _____

Your Top Goals: *December*

Monthly Financial Plan

Projected income: _____

Projected or possible income sources: _____

This month's coaching clients: _____

This month's prospects, or people to follow up with: _____

Total coaching slots to be filled: _____

Actual slots filled at the beginning of the month: _____

This month's business expenses: _____

This month's $$ to tax account: _____

This month's projected profit (income - taxes and business expenses): _____

Monthly Plan: *December*

Who will you reach out to for help? _____

_____

_____

Who will hold you accountable? _____

_____

_____

In what resources will you invest? _____

_____

_____

What is your income goal, and where will it come from? (names and events) _____

_____

_____

_____

Who are your top 3 prospects for future business?

     1.

     2.

     3.

What are you creating now to come to fruition over the next 90 days? _____

_____

_____

_____

How will you stay visible through networking? *(people, events- how? What? When?)* _____

_____

_____

_____

What results do you intend to get through these networking actions? _____

_____

_____

_____

How many people do you intend to add to your database this month? _____

Consult your plan you made for the year to keep on track.

December Monthly *Plan* Continued

What is your theme for the month? _____

Monthly (or more often) newsletter:
Use the template for creating your newsletter located under resources (pg. 261) to guide you.
There are 12 included, so please copy and use (I permit you) if you are doing a more regular
newsletter. Mine is weekly as of January 2020, but was monthly for 12 years prior!

Schedule the date or days you will send your newsletter out on your monthly calendar.

Social media plan*: (find clients, increase following) **See the expanded Social Media Plan on*
page 315 for additional planning guidance! _____
_____
_____
_____

Where will you post, and how often? _____
_____
_____
_____

What content will you share? *Have a separate notebook for sketching out social media content if*
necessary. _____
_____
_____
_____

How often and on what platforms will you go live? *Schedule days, times, and topics into your*
monthly calendar. _____
_____
_____
_____

What are your specific goals around your social media actions? _____
_____
_____
_____

Ideas

Monthly Overview: *December*

Monthly Theme: _____

Sunday	Monday	Tuesday	Wednesday
28	29	30	1
5	6	7	8
12	13	14	15
19	20	21	22
26	27	28	29
2	3	4	5

Thursday	Friday	Saturday	Notes
2	3	4	Income goal:
			Top three prospects: 1.
9	10	11	2.
			3.
16	17	18	Networking events this month:
23	24	25	
			Events to work on this month for the future (90 day outlook):
30	31		
6	7	8	

Week One: *December*

29 *Monday*

30 *Tuesday*

1 *Wednesday*

2 *Thursday*

Top Three Goals:
1.
2.
3.

3 *Friday*

4 *Saturday*

5 *Sunday*

Additional Notes:

Review + Action Plan

Use this page as you prepare for the week ahead, during Sunday planning time.

What went well last week? _____

_____

What did not go so well? _____

_____

What did you learn? _____

_____

What will you do differently this week because of what you learned? _____

_____

Projects to work on this week and top three actions to take with each:

    (write each activity into your schedule right now)

       1.

       2.

       3.

Prospects to follow up on: _____

_____

Obstacles that could get in your way: _____

_____

Solutions for facing possible obstacles: _____

_____

_____

Three things you are most grateful for:

       1.

       2.

       3.

What is your mantra or affirmation for the week? *(write it and repeat it often!)* _____

_____

_____

What you are reading this week: _____

_____

What you are listening to this week: _____

_____

Ideas

Week Two: *December*

6 *Monday*

7 *Tuesday*

8 *Wednesday*

9 *Thursday*

Top Three Goals:
  1.
  2.
  3.

10 *Friday*

11 *Saturday*

12 *Sunday*

Additional Notes:

Review + Action Plan

Use this page as you prepare for the week ahead, during Sunday planning time.

What went well last week? _____

_____

What did not go so well? _____

_____

What did you learn? _____

_____

What will you do differently this week because of what you learned? _____

_____

Projects to work on this week and top three actions to take with each:

    (write each activity into your schedule right now)

      1.

      2.

      3.

Prospects to follow up on: _____

_____

Obstacles that could get in your way: _____

_____

Solutions for facing possible obstacles: _____

_____

_____

Three things you are most grateful for:

      1.

      2.

      3.

What is your mantra or affirmation for the week? *(write it and repeat it often!)* _____

_____

_____

What you are reading this week: _____

_____

What you are listening to this week: _____

_____

Ideas

Week Three: *December*

13 *Monday*

14 *Tuesday*

15 *Wednesday*

16 *Thursday*

Top Three Goals:

1.

2.

3.

17 *Friday*

18 *Saturday*

19 *Sunday*

Additional Notes:

Review + Action Plan

Use this page as you prepare for the week ahead, during Sunday planning time.

What went well last week? _____

_____

What did not go so well? _____

_____

What did you learn? _____

_____

What will you do differently this week because of what you learned? _____

_____

Projects to work on this week and top three actions to take with each:

    (write each activity into your schedule right now)

      1.

      2.

      3.

Prospects to follow up on: _____

_____

Obstacles that could get in your way: _____

_____

Solutions for facing possible obstacles: _____

_____

_____

Three things you are most grateful for:

      1.

      2.

      3.

What is your mantra or affirmation for the week? *(write it and repeat it often!)* _____

_____

_____

What you are reading this week: _____

_____

What you are listening to this week: _____

Ideas

Week **Four**: *December*

20 *Monday*

21 *Tuesday*

22 *Wednesday*

23 *Thursday*

Top Three Goals:

1.

2.

3.

24 *Friday*

25 *Saturday*

26 *Sunday*

Additional Notes:

Review + Action Plan

Use this page as you prepare for the week ahead, during Sunday planning time.

What went well last week? _____

_____

What did not go so well? _____

_____

What did you learn? _____

_____

What will you do differently this week because of what you learned? _____

_____

Projects to work on this week and top three actions to take with each:

    (write each activity into your schedule right now)

      1.

      2.

      3.

Prospects to follow up on: _____

_____

Obstacles that could get in your way: _____

_____

Solutions for facing possible obstacles: _____

_____

_____

Three things you are most grateful for:

      1.

      2.

      3.

What is your mantra or affirmation for the week? *(write it and repeat it often!)* _____

_____

What you are reading this week: _____

_____

What you are listening to this week: _____

_____

Ideas

Week **Five:** *December*

27 *Monday*

28 *Tuesday*

29 *Wednesday*

30 *Thursday*

Top Three Goals:

1.

2.

3.

31 *Friday*

1 *Saturday*

2 *Sunday*

Additional Notes:

Review + Action Plan

Use this page as you prepare for the week ahead, during Sunday planning time.

What went well last week? _____

_____

What did not go so well? _____

_____

What did you learn? _____

_____

What will you do differently this week because of what you learned? _____

_____

Projects to work on this week and top three actions to take with each:

    (write each activity into your schedule right now)

      1.

      2.

      3.

Prospects to follow up on: _____

_____

Obstacles that could get in your way: _____

_____

Solutions for facing possible obstacles: _____

_____

_____

Three things you are most grateful for:

      1.

      2.

      3.

What is your mantra or affirmation for the week? *(write it and repeat it often!)* _____

_____

_____

What you are reading this week: _____

_____

What you are listening to this week:_____

_____

Monthly Reflection: *December*

It's time for your FOURTH QUARTER review! Please flip to page 314 to get it done!

What went well?

_____

_____

_____

_____

What are you most proud of?

_____

_____

_____

_____

What goals did you achieve?

_____

_____

_____

_____

What did not go so well?

_____

_____

_____

_____

What did you learn?

_____

_____

_____

_____

What will you do differently based on what you have learned?

_____

_____

_____

Total income: _____

Coaching Resources

S.M.A.R.T. *Goals*

Specific
Measurable
Actionable
Realistic
Time-based

Use these to set healthy goals for yourself and your clients, too!

When you run your goals through this list, you will set better goals and
raise your chances of achieving them!

Here's an example of one of my SMART goals:

I will write 1000 words a day Monday-Friday at 8:30-9:30 am in October, November and December, which will lead me to having 3 chapters of my book written within 90 days.

It is *specific* about writing, the time frame and the desired outcome.

It is *measurable* because there are numbers included and that is easy to measure.

It is *achievable* because this is something I can do- I have the ability and the time can be set aside.

It is *relevant* because I am going to make progress directly on one of my major goals.

It is *time-based* - days and times of day and for how long I will commit.

Powerful *Self-Coaching* Questions

Who do I have to become in order to be the coach who _____ ?

What am I willing to give up to make time or space for _____ ?

What beliefs do I have that stop me from being the coach that I want to be?
If I believed the opposite, what would that be?

What's the truth?
What's truer than that?

What stops me from offering my services to others?

What singular action could I take right now to move my business forward?

How can I fit more of the things I love to do into my schedule?
Work? Personal?

What is my reason for being a coach?

What am I grateful for in my coaching business?

What skills, if I developed them, would make me a better coach?

What are my personal and professional development plans?

What parts of my work energize me the most?
And how will I make sure to do more of these?

What are my top 5 strengths?
How can I use these strengths more on purpose?

What is my definition of success?

What does a "perfect day" look like for me?

How do I consistently challenge myself?

Your *Walk The Talk* Checklist

Make a list to help you stay on track with growing a flourishing business with the right clients. Do a check-in once a month to see how you are doing. You are a walking, talking billboard for your business. You represent the life and results that your clients wish to have, making you attractive as a coach.

❏   My physical self reflects energy and excellence. I exercise and fuel my body appropriately. My look, dress, grooming, body language, and attitude are all in sync, visibly positive.

❏   I am consistent in engaging in my learning and growth. I always have at least one coach that I am actively working with to become the best version of myself. I challenge myself on purpose to keep mentally sharp. I keep my mental clutter clear by taking daily actions that support it.

❏   I fearlessly discover what is holding me back in my own life and face each resistance. I am honest and vulnerable to create breakthroughs in my own life.

❏   My spirit is clear and light. I am active daily in making progress to keep it that way.

❏   My daily habits support me in living a positive lifestyle- body, mind, and spirit. I build positive energy in my business through the activities I engage in.

❏   I consistently ask myself, "Who do I have to become to create the life I want to live?" and "Who do I have to become to attract the right clients for me?"

❏   I talk about what I do as a coach, rather than holding back. I am bold in inviting people to explore my services and share the type of results my clients are getting. I ask for referrals and prospects for clients several days a week.

❏   I am fierce in the pursuit of helping my clients reach their goals. I honor that they have the answers and that I am not here to give them answers but to help them find their own.

❏   I rely on my strengths to help me with both projects and challenges. I know my strengths, and I use them on purpose. I purposely take on challenges to grow my resilience.

❏   I know who I am and what my purpose is.

❏   I organize my life and my business practices. I endeavor to become more organized every day.

"The way you live your life shows people who you are and why they should hire you."
~ Kimberly DuBrul

Your *'Perfect Client'* Description

Knowing who your perfect client is will help you to attract the right clients. I suggest creating a checklist out of your description. When you have a coaching inquiry, you can check the list to see if they are a match for you. *You only have to take the wrong client once to see the importance of this idea.*

Use your checklist to assure that you ask the right questions to discern whether or not this person or opportunity is right for you.

Aim for between 5-10 bullet points. Write your own, make them personal to you, and tweak them as you discover who your perfect client is.

An excellent way to start is to think about a client whom you have really enjoyed coaching. **What is it about them that you appreciate?**

A few ideas to get you started:

- They pay on time.
- They are working on goals that compliment my skills.
- They are in a specific industry.
- They are coachable.
- They are choosing coaching for themselves. *(vs. being made to engage in coaching.)*
- They have a particular personality or personality traits. *(be specific.)*

It is natural to want to help everyone, and you may not even know who your perfect client is yet. As you move forward and work with clients who are not right for you, you will put the pieces together.

Sometimes it helps to develop a descriptive list of what you don't want in a client. Make a list of these things and then ask yourself, "what is the opposite of each?"

Write your perfect client description below:
(come back to review/tweak during your quarterly reviews.)

_____
_____
_____
_____
_____
_____
_____
_____

Newsletter *Checklist + Ideas*

Frequency. Mine was monthly for many years, and in 2020 I made the move to weekly. Pick a consistent day of the week to develop it and schedule it to go out on the same day/time each week that you send it. People will count on it and look forward to it.

Theme. I suggest you connect your newsletter to a monthly theme that compliments your social media posts, blog posts, and newsletters.

Use a **product** like Constant Contact (I have used it for many years) to design your newsletter and to help you to build your database. There are many products out there- do some research and choose the one the suits you best.

Think about the **components** you would like in your newsletter.

Here are a few of mine to get you started; let them spark your own to make your newsletter reflect who you are and what your audience finds interesting.

- Special subject line- *changes each time*
- Welcome, introduction paragraph
- A video of me *(5 minutes or less)* expanding on the theme for the month
- A link to my blog post
- A link to my podcast
- Clickable PDF flyers with links to sign up for current offerings
- Book, magazine, podcast, and other resource recommendations
- A quote
- All of the buttons to connect with you on social media
- A link to your website and a way to communicate with you
- A quiz or poll
- A contest
- A giveaway like a printable checklist, chart, list, or other freebie
- Ask that they forward it to others who might find the information valuable

Sign up to receive my weekly newsletter at www.kimberlydubrul.com.

Capture all of your ideas for possible newsletter themes, items, shares, books, or other concepts that you can pull from all year long:

_____

_____

_____

_____

Quarterly Review *Planning*

Take a day, half-day- or even a couple of days each quarter to retreat and work on your business.

If possible, you can go away and stay somewhere away from home. Depending upon where you live and your circumstances, you can create day trips, like coffee shop hopping or even buckling into one place for a day at a time. I like planning and retreating outside, weather depending. It's my go-to in the spring, summer, and part of the fall. In the wintertime, I love a cozy fireplace setting.

I've even held my quarterly retreats at a spa. If/when it is safe to do so, put yourself into a relaxing environment and intersperse your planning with movement, and maybe a massage to help you access your best ideas. Maybe you know someone with a cottage or cabin, or maybe you take yourself to the ocean. Or perhaps you go to your backyard like I do these days.

We are all in different seasons of life. Whatever you can do to sliver out some time for your planning is helpful. Two hours is better than not taking any time.

Do what you can do, be creative, and enjoy. Oh, and THINK BIG!

Ideas

Places I can hold my quarterly retreat:
Make a list of all of the possibilities. Plan ahead and set the dates for the year, and make any reservations. Scheduling your reservation will likely cause you to follow through.

_____
_____
_____
_____

What resources will I bring with me?
Make sure you have everything you need to plan, read, and work.
Create a checklist and pack up in advance.

What is my agenda?
Creating one will ensure you stay on track with priorities.

Quarter One Review

Where am I financially?
Income received: _____
Expenses incurred: _____
Am I profitable? _____
What would I like to change or expand in this area over the next quarter? _____
_____
_____

What went well in the past quarter? _____
_____

What am I most proud of? _____

What goals did I accomplish? _____

What is left unfinished? _____
What is still important? _____
What have I learned? _____
_____

What will I do differently in the next quarter? _____
_____

What will I intend to learn/study/read in the next 90 days? _____
_____

What projects will I start or move forward? _____
_____

What are my top 3 goals for the next quarter?
    1.
    2.
    3.
Who would I like to connect with? _____

What skill/s would I like to learn or expand? _____
_____

What affirmation/s will I use? _____
_____

Quarter Two Review

Where am I financially?
Income received: _____
Expenses incurred: _____
Am I profitable? _____
What would I like to change or expand in this area over the next quarter? _____
_____
_____

What went well in the past quarter? _____
_____
_____

What am I most proud of? _____

What goals did I accomplish? _____

What is left unfinished? _____
What is still important? _____
What have I learned? _____
_____

What will I do differently in the next quarter? _____
_____

What will I intend to learn/study/read in the next 90 days? _____
_____

What projects will I start or move forward? _____
_____

What are my top 3 goals for the next quarter?
    1.
    2.
    3.
Who would I like to connect with? _____

What skill/s would I like to learn or expand? _____
_____

What affirmation/s will I use? _____
_____

Quarter Three Review

Where am I financially?
Income received: _____
Expenses incurred:_____
Am I profitable? _____
What would I like to change or expand in this area over the next quarter? _____
_____
_____

What went well in the past quarter? _____
_____
_____

What am I most proud of? _____
_____

What goals did I accomplish? _____
_____

What is left unfinished? _____
What is still important? _____
What have I learned? _____
_____
_____

What will I do differently in the next quarter? _____
_____
_____

What will I intend to learn/study/read in the next 90 days? _____
_____
_____

What projects will I start or move forward? _____
_____
_____

What are my top 3 goals for the next quarter?
     1.
     2.
     3.
Who would I like to connect with? _____
_____

What skill/s would I like to learn or expand? _____
_____
_____

What affirmation/s will I use? _____
_____

Quarter Four Review

Where am I financially?

Income received: _____

Expenses incurred:_____

Am I profitable? _____

What would I like to change or expand in this area over the next quarter? _____
_____
_____

What went well in the past quarter? _____
_____

What am I most proud of? _____

What goals did I accomplish? _____

What is left unfinished? _____

What is still important? _____

What have I learned? _____
_____

What will I do differently in the next quarter? _____
_____

What will I intend to learn/study/read in the next 90 days? _____
_____

What projects will I start or move forward? _____
_____

What are my top 3 goals for the next quarter?

     1.

     2.

     3.

Who would I like to connect with? _____

What skill/s would I like to learn or expand? _____
_____

What affirmation/s will I use? _____
_____

Social Media *Plan*

Media	Y/N	When	Frequency	Theme/Subject
Twitter				
Instagram				
Instagram *Stories*				
Instagram *IGTV*				
LinkedIn				
LinkedIn *Articles*				
TikTok				
Facebook				
Facebook *Stories*				
Facebook *Live*				
Other *Social Media*				

Project Planning: *January*

Project Name: _____

What is important to you about doing this project? _____

What will the results be of you finishing and launching it? _____

Timeline: _____

Benchmarks: _____

Who can help? _____
What resources do I need? _____

Information/research needed: _____

My schedule to work on it and get it done: _____

Project Planning: *February*

Project Name: _____

What is important to you about doing this project? _____

What will the results be of you finishing and launching it? _____

Timeline: _____

Benchmarks: _____

Who can help? _____
What resources do I need? _____

Information/research needed: _____

My schedule to work on it and get it done: _____

Project Planning: *March*

Project Name: _____

What is important to you about doing this project? _____

_____

What will the results be of you finishing and launching it? _____

_____

Timeline: _____

_____

_____

Benchmarks: _____

_____

_____

Who can help? _____

What resources do I need? _____

_____

Information/research needed: _____

_____

My schedule to work on it and get it done: _____

_____

_____

Project Planning: *April*

Project Name: _____

What is important to you about doing this project? _____

_____

What will the results be of you finishing and launching it? _____

_____

Timeline: _____

_____

_____

Benchmarks: _____

_____

_____

Who can help? _____

What resources do I need? _____

_____

Information/research needed: _____

_____

My schedule to work on it and get it done: _____

_____

Project Planning: *May*

Project Name: _____

What is important to you about doing this project? _____

What will the results be of you finishing and launching it? _____

Timeline: _____

Benchmarks: _____

Who can help? _____
What resources do I need? _____

Information/research needed: _____

My schedule to work on it and get it done: _____

Project Planning: *June*

Project Name: _____

What is important to you about doing this project? _____

What will the results be of you finishing and launching it? _____

Timeline: _____

Benchmarks: _____

Who can help? _____
What resources do I need? _____

Information/research needed: _____

My schedule to work on it and get it done: _____

Project Planning: *July*

Project Name: _____

What is important to you about doing this project? _____

What will the results be of you finishing and launching it? _____

Timeline: _____

Benchmarks: _____

Who can help? _____
What resources do I need? _____

Information/research needed: _____

My schedule to work on it and get it done: _____

Project Planning: *August*

Project Name: _____

What is important to you about doing this project? _____

What will the results be of you finishing and launching it? _____

Timeline: _____

Benchmarks: _____

Who can help? _____
What resources do I need? _____

Information/research needed: _____

My schedule to work on it and get it done: _____

Project Planning: *September*

Project Name: _____

What is important to you about doing this project? _____

_____

What will the results be of you finishing and launching it? _____

_____

Timeline: _____

_____

_____

Benchmarks: _____

_____

_____

Who can help? _____

What resources do I need? _____

_____

Information/research needed: _____

_____

My schedule to work on it and get it done: _____

_____

_____

Project Planning: *October*

Project Name: _____

What is important to you about doing this project? _____

_____

What will the results be of you finishing and launching it? _____

_____

Timeline: _____

_____

_____

Benchmarks: _____

_____

Who can help? _____

What resources do I need? _____

_____

Information/research needed: _____

_____

My schedule to work on it and get it done: _____

Project Planning: *November*

Project Name: _____

What is important to you about doing this project? _____
_____

What will the results be of you finishing and launching it? _____
_____

Timeline: _____
_____
_____

Benchmarks: _____
_____
_____

Who can help? _____

What resources do I need? _____
_____

Information/research needed: _____
_____

My schedule to work on it and get it done: _____
_____
_____

Project Planning: *December*

Project Name: _____

What is important to you about doing this project? _____
_____

What will the results be of you finishing and launching it? _____
_____

Timeline: _____
_____
_____

Benchmarks: _____
_____
_____

Who can help? _____

What resources do I need? _____
_____

Information/research needed: _____
_____

My schedule to work on it and get it done: _____
_____

Additional Resources

Suggested Reading

The Compound Effect, *Darren Hardy*
Vibrate Higher Daily, *Lalah Delia*
Everyone Communicates, Few Connect , *John Maxwell*
The 15 Invaluable Laws of Growth, *John Maxwell*
Range, *David Epstein*
Deep Work, *Cal Newport*
Mindset, *Carol Dweck*
Talking to Strangers, *Malcolm Gladwell*
Mastery, *Robert Greene*
More Than Enough, *Elaine Welteroth*
Your 5 Minute Personal Coach, *Valorie Burton*
Big Magic, *Elizabeth Gilbert*
The Path Made Clear, *Oprah Winfrey*

Audio

The 3 Day Effect, on Audible by *Florence Williams*
Challenge Accepted, by *James Woosley*
Unlocking Us, podcast with *Brene Brown*
Compete to Create, on Audible by *Pete Carroll*
Power Moves, on Audible by *Adam Grant*

Products/Other

VIA Character Strengths Assessment
www.viacharacter.com
ICF Core Competencies
https://coachfederation.org/core-competencies
Nike Running Club app
Quotes Creator app
Panda Planner
www.pandaplanner.com
Self Care, card deck by *Cheryl Richardson*
Insight Timer Meditation app
Goodreads app
The CaPP Institute - Coach Training, Coach Certification, Coaching
https://cappinstitute.com

Ideas

"Each person holds so much power within themselves that needs to be let out. Sometimes they just need a little nudge, a little support, a little coaching and the greatest things can happen." Pete Carroll

Ideas

"A good coach can change a game, a GREAT coach can change a life."
Coach John Wooden

Ideas

Ideas

Ideas

Ideas

Ideas

Ideas

"Take mindful actions and then surrender to and trust the process. Do this over and over and over again." Kimberly DuBrul

Ideas

"Let the resistance be there, but don't resist the resistance."
David R. Hawkins

Ideas

Ideas

Ideas

"There is a big difference between processing and complaining."
Taryn Toomey

>>>———————————<<<

Ideas

Ideas

Kimberly DuBrul, PCC has been a coach for 18 years. Starting out as a business coach, she added life and mindset coaching to her offerings in 2008. She is a

coach's coach, a coach trainer and teacher for the CaPP Institute's Coach Training Intensive and Certification programs. She works with individuals, groups, is a speaker on many topics and offers retreats, webinars, teleclasses, mastermind groups and

more. Most of all, she believes in the power of coaching and the difference it can make in someone's life. For more about Kimberly's experience, background and expertise, please visit her website at www.kimberlydubrul.com.

Make sure to order your
2022 Business Development & Planning Calendar!

Made in the USA
Monee, IL
04 January 2021